THE MODERN UNIVERSE

The Modern Universe

RAYMOND A. LYTTLETON

With line drawings by A. Spark

and 16 pages of plates

READERS UNION

HODDER & STOUGHTON

London 1957

"It was just after this adventure that we encountered a continent of immense extent and of prodigious solidity, but which, nevertheless, was supported entirely upon the back of a sky-blue cow that had no fewer than four-hundred horns."

"*That*, now, I believe," said the king, "because I have read something of the kind before, in a book."

EDGAR ALLAN POE (The Thousand-and-Second Tale of Scheherazade).

This RU edition was produced in 1958 for sale to its members only by Readers Union Ltd at 38 William IV Street, Charing Cross, London, W.C.2, and at Letchworth Garden City, Hertfordshire. Full details of membership may be obtained from our London address. The book is set in 11 point Plantin, one point leaded, and has been reprinted and bound by the Camelot Press Ltd, London and Southampton. It was first published in 1956 by Hodder & Stoughton Ltd.

PREFACE

This book is based on a series of six programmes given over the Television Service of the B.B.C. during the autumn of 1955, but is in fact a considerably expanded version. As in the original talks, I have again tried as far as possible to avoid technicalities and put things in a way intelligible to ordinary readers. The inclusion of photographs of many of the principal astronomical phenomena seemed to me essential, and I have to express my special thanks for permission to reproduce these pictures to the Directors of the several observatories and other institutions with which the photographs are associated.

It may be questioned whether there is any point in telling the man-in-the-street about astronomical matters that apparently have no bearing on his everyday existence. My own attitude to this rests on two considerations. First, it is the man-in-the-street who by his more mundane but indispensable work provides among other things the necessary leisure for scientists to devote themselves to study and make discoveries, some of which gradually change the whole character of society. So by way of return there is an element of duty for scientists occasionally to give some account of progress in their subject to those sufficiently interested, but who otherwise would have little opportunity to learn anything of such things. I believe that deep down in almost everyone there slumbers what Clifford called "cosmic emotion," and no branch of science more than astronomy tends to arouse this feeling, which must have its roots in man's instinctive desire to comprehend his relationship to the mysterious world in which he finds himself. The discoveries of modern astronomy have led to a conception of this world far different and far in advance of anything that might ever have been conjectured, and it is clearly desirable that some

5

straightforward account of these modern advances should be available to supplant earlier popular works based on older and less complete views of the universe.

Also, there appears to me a further urgent reason why people should be informed of the penetrating achievements of science and led to realise its future possibilities. And that is the steadily emerging conclusion, which science itself is forcing on us, that almost all that has hitherto passed for knowledge and understanding in other fields, such as political theory, philosophy, and ethics, to mention only a few, will eventually be relegated to the level of mere rationalisation: that is, associated "explanations" having no real validity.[1] But if this happens and becomes widely appreciated, so that in turn the ordinary man and woman lose faith in these things and the assumptions based on them, what is to be put in their place? The answer seems to be that the only hope lies in science itself, which is steadily rendering obsolete and superseding all the older systems of thought. Nothing can really be gained by holding views that have no valid basis, and it seems more than probable that we shall do better as a community to the extent that we can bring something of the scientific attitude to bear on the unending range of problems that inevitably have somehow to be dealt with. But first it will be necessary to develop much more general confidence in science, and there seems no other way to do this than by making clear something of its achievements and gradually putting people in a position to judge for themselves. My original talks and the present volume represent very small contributions to this large and important objective, but one which it will certainly take time to achieve.

I should perhaps emphasise that this book is not claimed to be a thoroughgoing treatise, far from it, but only a brief popular account of some of the modern advances and problems of the stronomical universe. Those wishing to pursue matters further will have no difficulty in finding abundant reading material for themselves, and I shall regard it as an added success if this little volume helps to set any young persons on the road to an

[1] Rationalisation has been defined as "The invention of 'satisfying' theories as opposed to 'satisfactory' ones."

6

interest in scientific study, with the infinite scope for ingenuity and attainment that it holds out to those prepared to take the necessary trouble when they are young to equip themselves for the work.

RAYMOND A. LYTTLETON.

March 1956.

CONTENTS

CONTENTS

IV. THE SUN

V. THE STARS AND GALAXY

VI. THE EXPANDING UNIVERSE

LIST OF ILLUSTRATIONS

between pages 80 and 81

13

KEY TO ACKNOWLEDGEMENTS

The illustrations listed above are reproduced by courtesy of the following:

[1]United States Navy.
[2]American Museum of Natural History.
[3]Lick Observatory.
[4]Mount Wilson and Palomar Observatories.
[5]Life Magazine.
[6]Professor Carl Störmer.
[7]McDonald Observatory.
[8]Dr. V. B. Meen, The Royal Ontario Museum.
[9]W. J. S. Lockyer.
[10]The Hayden Planetarium of the American Museum of Natural History.
[11]Victoria and Albert Museum, Crown Copyright.
[12]E. E. Barnard.
[13]Dr. Jan Hogböm.
[14]Royal Greenwich Observatory.
[15]Dr. H. von Klüber, Cambridge Expedition.
[16]Dr. M. Ryle, Cavendish Laboratory.
[17]Franklin Adams.
[18]Lowell Observatory.
[19]*Picture Post* Library.

I
THE EARTH

The age of the Earth—Uranium-lead method—
What a finite age implies—Need for an origin—
Dimensions and properties—Relation to moon
and sun—Light-year—Determination of distances—Eros—Effect of sun's light—Night and
day — Seasons — Midnight sun — Date-line —
Earth's magnetism—Interior of the Earth—
Rocky shell—Liquid core—Earthquakes—Push-
and Shake-waves—Composition of Earth—Origin
of magnetic field—Precession of Earth's axis.

THE AGE OF THE EARTH

Have you ever wondered how old this Earth of ours is? A few generations ago it must have seemed utterly impossible that this could ever be found out, but the discovery of radioactivity has opened a royal road to the dating of the past and has made the determination of great intervals of time as trustworthy, or even more trustworthy, than the measurement of great distances in space.

It has been established that the Earth is in round numbers four thousand million years old: or as it is usually written by astronomers 4×10^9 years. This is the age of the oldest known rocks in the outer layers of the Earth. So if we go back longer than this in time, these outer layers simply cannot have been there, and if the Earth was formed as a whole it must mean that there would in fact be no Earth. If the Earth formed by gradual accretion at its surface, as now seems possible, the age determinations refer only to the outermost layers, and a unique "age of the Earth" may not exist. But if the process took a short time compared with 4×10^9 years, then we can nevertheless regard this as the age, just as we speak of the age of a building and ignore the period of construction. So something must have happened about four thousand million years ago to bring the Earth into being, and there immediately arises the intriguing question of what that something was, and how it happened.

Now how is this age found out? Obviously what is needed is something in the nature of a clock, some steadily occurring process, operating after the manner of an hour-glass, that we can examine and see what stage it has reached, and this is exactly what radioactivity provides. You may remember how

17

Sherlock Holmes in one of his cases ["The Camberwell Poison-
ing Case" (unpublished); see "The Five Orange Pips," 1887.]
proved by winding up the dead man's watch that it had been
fully wound up only two hours before, and therefore that its
owner must have gone to bed within that time. Certain
radioactive elements, such as uranium, work rather like this,
except that they cannot be wound up again as can a watch,
and enable us to prove that they must have become enclosed in
the rocks now containing them these thousands of millions of
years ago.

The way radioactivity manifests itself is now well known. If
we take a piece of radioactive material, such as uranium, a
definite small fraction of all its atoms break down every second
and each one ejects at high speed a so-called alpha particle,
which is really the nucleus of the helium atom and so carries
an electric charge that enables it to be detected. The atom left
behind goes through a series of changes before finally settling
down as an atom of lead, while for each one so changed there
have been ejected eight atoms of helium. The processes concerned can be studied directly and they turn out to be entirely
unaffected by any changes in pressure, or temperature, or any
chemical recombination of the atoms concerned, or indeed by
any ordinary influences. This is because the changes involve
only the so-called nucleus of the atom and not the surrounding
electrons that give it its more familiar properties.

The ejected charged particles can be detected and the number ejected in any given time measured by means of an electrical
apparatus called a Geiger-counter (Fig. 1). So the number of
atoms of a measured quantity of any radioactive element that
break up every second can be found. With uranium for example,
if we think of a given amount, say 1oz in a sealed container,
[One ounce of pure uranium contains about 7×10^{22} atoms i.e.
seventy thousand million million million atoms.] Then in one
million years $\frac{1}{6,500}$ of the uranium atoms would have broken
down and an equal number of lead atoms appeared in their
place; and always the same proportion would change every
succeeding million years. In one thousand million years this
means that just about one-sixth of the uranium would have

changed to lead (Fig. 2). At any stage a chemical analysis of the material determining the ratio of uranium to lead would give

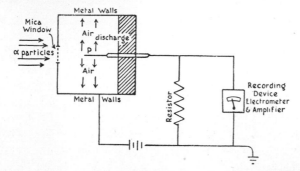

Fig. 1

Schematic diagram of a Geiger-counter for recording charged particles. A potential difference is maintained between the metallic point P and the metallic walls just insufficient to cause electric discharge across the air-filled container. An electrified particle moving in at high speed through the mica window starts the discharge. The resistance then limits the current and interrupts the discharges. Successive discharges can be recorded by an amplifier connected with the circuit

the time interval since the material was a hundred per cent pure uranium. This is how it has been proved that pieces of

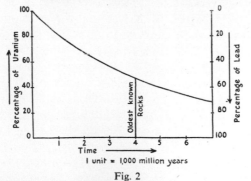

Fig. 2

Graph of decay of uranium, showing how the percentage decreases with time and the percentage of lead correspondingly increases

rock which we can actually handle began their existence as rocks thousands of millions of years ago and have lain buried in the Earth for these aeons of time until in very recent years some miner's pick came along to prise them from their resting place.

The requisite conditions have actually occurred, and igneous rocks are occasionally found containing uranium minerals compacted into them so that no extraneous substances, such as water for instance, can have disturbed the contents since they were laid down. Chemical analysis of the amounts of uranium and lead, then gives the age, provided of course there was no lead in the rock originally. But here again Nature has been very helpful, because the lead into which the uranium changes is not identical with ordinary lead. The uranium lead is of atomic weight 206 whereas that of ordinary lead is 207, and this makes it possible to allow for its presence when necessary.

The ages of many eruptive rocks have now been measured by these means, and they follow exactly the epochs already otherwise determined by geologists from the strata in which they are found. Carboniferous eruptions are two hundred and fifty million years old, early pre-Cambrian ones about five hundred million years, and the oldest pre-Cambrian fifteen hundred million years. The very oldest specimens of all give ages of just about four thousand million years. These ages are confirmed by other variants of the radioactive method, such as the measurement of the helium still remaining in the rock, and are also confirmed in order of magnitude by the ages of meteorites, and other more or less independent considerations as we shall see.

So the upshot of all this is that about four thousand million years ago the Earth must somehow have been formed and started on its career; and one of the ultimate problems of astronomy is to find out how this can have occurred. By "finding out" is meant, not simply conjecturing a general verbal account and asserting that it is so, after the manner of the apologues of Genesis, but obtaining a solution that will really explain the origin in terms of scientific processes, and satisfy the rigours of mathematical and critical analysis when these are applied to test whether the theory is in accordance with established dynamical and physical principles.

As can be imagined, it is not an easy problem. Indeed, it

cannot really be commenced until we know what the Earth as
a whole is made of, what its properties are, and which of these
may be relevant to the problem in hand. Also, having obtained
some knowledge of these, we would next need to know what
building materials may have been available for its formation.
And then, if we had judged that the time had come when we
might start on the problem itself, we would be faced with one
of the most difficult parts of all, namely that of thinking out
possible ways in which the available materials might come to
form the Earth; in other words the theoretical difficulty of
reconstructing what has happened in the remote past to produce
the present situation.

It is obviously not possible therefore to start straight in on
the problem; and although many theories of the formation of
the Earth have been proposed in the past, most, if not all, have
turned out to have been based on knowledge inadequate for the
purpose. But it must not for one moment be thought that such
attempts, some of which later on have seemed very superficial,
are therefore to be deprecated, for right or wrong such theories
serve to give a kind of directive to future research and form a
general centre to which many diverse lines of progress can be
referred, to see if they reinforce or contradict each other even
though in the end we still may not get a final solution to the
problem of the origin of the Earth.

Besides study of the Earth itself, an essential preliminary will
be to find what association the Earth has with the sun and other
neighbouring bodies at the present time, which is open to
practical examination, and then to find how these associations
may have changed in the past, which can only be done by
theoretical means. So in this way, the question of the age of the
Earth leads to the consideration of its origin, and this leads to
the consideration of other astronomical bodies, the planets and
comets, the sun and the stars; and in turn it has finally com-
pelled scientists to consider the great question of the universe
as a whole.

Although the processes of the origin and formation of the
Earth are still only very imperfectly understood, the foregoing
remarks show how recognition of the existence of the problem

serves to bring about a general attack upon it that inevitably takes us by successive stages from the Earth itself to the limits of the universe. This in outline sets the general pattern of this series of studies.

THE EARTH ITSELF

Let us begin therefore by coming back to the Earth itself. Quite apart from its constitution, all our astronomical observations are necessarily made from it, and so the measurement of the Earth is another essential preliminary.

The following are the main features of the Earth:

The Earth is a large almost spherical body nearly eight thousand miles in diameter, and almost twenty-five thousand miles in circumference.

The average density of the whole Earth is just over five and a half times that of water, and so its total weight in tons is 6×10^{21}; that is six thousand million million million tons.

It turns completely round on its axis, through the north and south poles, once every twenty-four (sidereal) hours. (In terms of our ordinary civil hours it takes 23 hours 56 minutes 4·091 seconds; the difference arises from the annual motion of the Earth round the sun.)

The Earth is slightly flattened towards the polar regions. The polar diameter is almost exactly 7,900 miles, but the equatorial diameter is $7,926\frac{2}{3}$ miles.

The flattening is due to the rotation which by centrifugal force tends to make the Earth bulge out at the equatorial regions, where the speed in the daily circle is just over a thousand miles an hour. In the latitude of England we are nearer the axis of rotation and the speed is only about six hundred miles an hour, and this is carrying us eastwards all the time; America is moving towards Europe where we are, and we are moving towards where Russia is, and so on.

This is only a small part of the motion we are undergoing. The Earth is travelling round the sun, and the moon along with it, at about $18\frac{1}{2}$ miles a second—nearly seventy thousand miles per hour. But it is all so perfectly uniform and steady that we are entirely unaware of it. As Eddington once said in speaking of the great distances that we travel through astronomical causes, so vast compared with those of our tiny earthly journeys, it is not travel itself that tires us but being put in a little box and shaken up.

Our Earth is simply one, and a pretty small one at that, of a set of several planets that all circle the sun. The Earth does this at an average distance from the sun of ninety-three million miles, and it takes it the whole year (365¼ days) to get once right round the sun as referred to the fixed background of stars. The path is not quite a circle but an ellipse of small eccentricity (one sixtieth) with the sun at a focus, and the sun's distance actually oscillates by about one and a half million miles on either side this average of ninety-three million miles. The sun is furthest from the Earth early in the month of July and nearest early in January.

Figure 3 shows the dimensions of the Earth, moon, and sun, and their distances apart, but no convenient diagram can represent the true proportions for the reason that the sun is so exceedingly large and distant compared with the sizes of the Earth and moon. Here are the actual values:

	Diameter (miles)	Distance apart (miles)
Moon	2160	
		239,000
Earth	7920	
		93,000,000
Sun	864,000	

If we tried to make a scale model of the Earth-moon-sun system that would go in any ordinary room, and took twenty feet as representing the sun's distance of ninety-three million miles, then the sun itself would be represented by a sphere of just over two inches in diameter, the Earth would be about one fiftieth of an inch in diameter—about half the size of a pinhead—and the moon about one two-hundredth of an inch in diameter moving round at about five eighths of an inch away from the Earth.

If we used any ordinary model of the Earth, such as the usual sized globe that maps of the world are put on, say about a foot and a half in diameter, the sun on that scale would be rather more than three miles away. This brings out how very far the sun is by our ordinary everyday standards of distance. Although it is 864,000 miles in diameter, we know how small it looks in the sky, and this is solely because of the vast distance of ninety-three million miles separating us from it. If we travelled by express train night and day, and never stopped, it would take

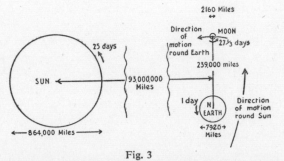

Fig. 3

Diagram showing sizes, *but not to scale*, of Earth, moon and sun. The arrows show the directions of motion, and rotation, as viewed from above the system on the northerly side, that is containing the Earth's north pole

nearly two hundred years to cover the distance—even if we could afford the £1,000,000 or so for the fare!

Now these large numbers come in simply because we are using as the unit of length our ordinary mile, which was of course adopted originally for the purpose of measuring local distances on Earth, when really it is quite inadequate for astronomical distances. It is about as if we had a car speedometer that recorded the distances in inches or centimetres. To avoid these and even much larger numbers that would otherwise keep cropping up, astronomers often measure distances by means of the speed of light, and refer to a distance in terms of the time light would take to traverse it. Now light travels at 186,000 miles per second. Light is a particular range of electromagnetic waves, and in empty space all such radiations travel with exactly this same speed. Radio-waves, for example, travel with the speed of light; so that the signals of radio and television programmes travel from the transmitter to the receiving aerials with the speed of light.

Radio waves (of a suitable kind) could therefore travel right round the Earth in just under one seventh of a second, and if the signals were strong enough it would be possible with powerful receiving equipment to hear someone's broadcast voice by two routes, once directly by a path a few miles long, say, and the other right round the Earth by a path nearly twenty-five thousand miles long (Fig. 4). We would hear everything twice over, but the second lot of words would each arrive

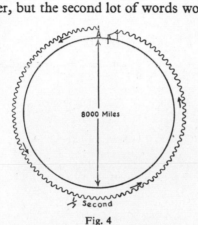

Fig. 4
Radio waves travel at 186,000 miles per second and could go right round the Earth in just under $\frac{1}{7}$ second

about one-seventh of a second late. This was actually done, with Howard Marshall providing the voice, a few years ago. So you see modern science can put a girdle round the Earth in a seventh of a second, never mind forty minutes.

In the following table are given the times that light (or radio waves) would take to travel to the Earth from the object named.

	Distance (miles)	Light Time
Moon	239,000	$1\frac{1}{4}$ seconds
Sun	93,000,000	8 minutes 20 seconds
Pluto	3,700,000,000	$5\frac{1}{2}$ hours

In this table is included Pluto, the furthest known planet of the solar system, which is about forty times as far from the sun as is the Earth. The moonlight we see is only reflected sunlight, so it has in fact first done the 8 minutes 20 seconds from the sun before bouncing off the moon to arrive at the Earth about $1\frac{1}{4}$ seconds later. Similarly, Pluto shines only by reflected light, which therefore has to do the $5\frac{1}{2}$ hours approximately (according to the precise positions of the Earth and Pluto) each way to get to us.

DETERMINATION OF DISTANCES

The distance of a comparatively near object like the moon, but which we cannot actually get to, can be determined by means of the application of simple geometry, as is illustrated in Fig. 5. The circle represents a section of the Earth, and L

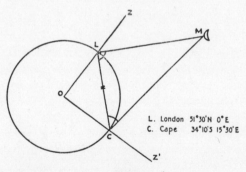

L. London   51°30'N 0°E
C. Cape   34°10'S 15°30'E

Fig. 5

Determination of the distance of the Moon. Measurement of the angles at the ends L and C of a base-line LC of known length enables the position of M to be found.

and C two observatories as far apart as conveniently possible and as nearly on the same meridian as possible. London and the Cape of Good Hope, for instance, are about six thousand miles apart and separated in longitude by only about 18 degrees. By means of a telescope the angular distance ZLM of a selected point on the Moon can be accurately found, as also can Z'CM at the same instant. So, in the triangle MLC the base length LC is known and also the angles at L and C, and as every schoolboy knows this settles the position of M. The longer the baseline the better and the more accurate the result.

This is the principle of all methods. Another application of it depends for the baseline on the distance that a single observatory is carried eastwards by the rotation of the Earth in a known time. All methods agree in giving the average distance of the Moon from the Earth, centre to centre, as 238,860 miles, which is just over sixty times the radius of the Earth itself.

The moon's path round the Earth is not circular, and the actual distance varies from 221,463 miles at its least value to 252,710 at its greatest. This variability has an important effect on the nature and duration of eclipses, as we shall see later. Once the size of the path round the Earth is known, the speed of the Moon can easily be found to average 2,290 miles per hour, and it takes on the average $27\frac{1}{3}$ days for it to go round the Earth.

This direct method of triangulation is of very limited accuracy when it comes to determining the distance of the sun, because of the very great distance compared with any terrestrial baseline. Now it happens that all the proportions of the solar system can be settled purely from observations of angular positions of the planets. This results from Kepler's so-called harmonic law, that the squares of the periods of the planets in their paths round the sun are proportional to the cubes of their distances from the sun; and the periods can be found without the measurement of any lengths. Accordingly, if any one length within the solar system is measured, all others follow. Now the nearer an object is to the Earth, the more accurately can its distance be found by this triangulation process, and this is one of the reasons why close approaches of Mars have in the past been important. At its nearest to us Mars is sometimes just under thirty-five million miles away, so clearly this distance will be capable of being measured more accurately than the measurement direct of the sun's distance.

A far more suitable object for the purpose was discovered in 1898 in the form of the tiny asteroid Eros, only about fifteen miles in average diameter, which at its closest is less than fourteen million miles from the Earth (Fig. 6). The most recent suitable close approach occurred in 1931 when the opportunity was taken for thousands of observations to be made of this minor planet at many observatories with a view to deriving the sun's distance. The results were not ready to be published till more than ten years later.

Fig. 6

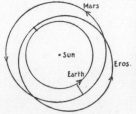

The orbit of the minor planet Eros in relation to those of Mars and the Earth. The closest possible distance of Eros is just under 14 million miles; in 1931 it came to within about 16 million miles of the Earth. Measurement of its distance enables the scale of the entire solar system to be found. The closest possible distance of Mars is just under 35 million miles; it will be nearly within this distance in September 1956. The nearer an object comes to the Earth, the more accurately can its distance and the scale of the solar system be found.

EFFECTS OF THE SUN'S LIGHT

The importance of the sun to the Earth and to ourselves cannot be exaggerated. It pours out a great flood of energy in the form of light and heat, and although the Earth intercepts only the tiniest fraction, we ourselves are utterly and absolutely dependent on it. If the sun's output were to cease suddenly, our days would be numbered, probably on the fingers of one hand. But there is not the smallest likelihood of any such calamity, quite otherwise. Many lines of evidence, astronomical, geological, and physical, combine to establish that the sun has been shining at much its present rate for at least five thousand million years, longer than the age of the Earth, but it has nevertheless used up only a few per cent of its great internal store of energy. It can easily go on for at least as long again and probably much longer. So the cessation of the sun's light and heat need not be regarded even as a possibility.

Let us consider then the simplest effects of this sunlight as it reaches the Earth. The sun is so far away that its light comes to the Earth as though it were a narrow parallel searchlight beam, and illuminates directly only one half of the surface at a time. But because of the surrounding air, which extends upwards in rarefied form for at least several hundred miles, light is reflected and scattered to give a twilight zone extending at gradually decreasing intensity to about 18° beyond the limit of the directly illuminated part of the Earth's surface. At the boundary of the shadow, on the side next to us in the diagram (Fig. 7), places

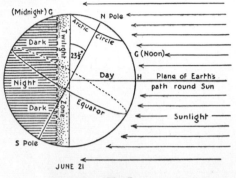

Fig. 7

The position of the Earth in relation to the incident sunlight at midsummer, 21 June about. The position of a place such as Greenwich (G) at noon and midnight are shown. For a place such as H the sun is directly overhead at noon

will just be moving into the light, and it is sunrise or dawn. On the opposite side places are just going farther into the shadow, and it is sunset or evening.

The north-south axis NS (Fig. 7) that the Earth turns round is not upright in regard to the general plane in which the Earth moves round the sun, but always slopes over at an angle of about $23\frac{1}{2}$ degrees, known as the obliquity of the ecliptic, meaning thereby the angle between the plane of the Earth's equator and the plane of the Earth's motion round the sun (in which eclipses occur).

On midsummer day, June 21, the northern end of this axis is over towards the Sun as much as possible (Fig. 7). The sun is the furthest north ($23\frac{1}{2}°$) of the equator it ever gets—the summer solstice. It therefore lights up more of the northern hemisphere than the southern one. The sun is overhead at noon at a place such as H situated $23\frac{1}{2}°$ north of the equator, that is on the tropic of Cancer, and north of this the days are at their longest. In a region surrounding the north pole a curious thing happens in that the sunlight shines on it all the time as the Earth rotates. This region extends $23\frac{1}{2}°$ south from the north pole, and the limit is the Arctic Circle. So on this day of the year for the whole twenty-four hours round the clock the sun does not set. This is the region of the so-called midnight sun. It does not reach down to any part of Britain, but it cuts across the northern part of Norway and Sweden.

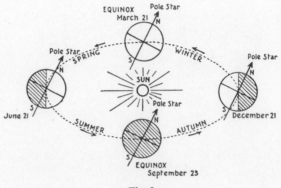

Fig. 8

The position and orientation of the Earth in relation to the sun at different times of year. The axis SN points always in the same direction (approximately to the Pole star) throughout the year

Simultaneously, an equal area round the south pole remains in perpetual darkness.

As the Earth moves round the sun in its yearly journey, the polar axis always stays in the same direction: that is, if there were a fixed pole-star in that direction the axis would always point towards that star. (There is no visible star in the precise direction, but the bright star Polaris is just over a degree away —about twice the width of the Moon.) Fig. 8 illustrates the successive positions of the Earth at three-month intervals from June 21. This shows that at about September 23 the polar axis is now perpendicular to the direction of the sun; in other words the sun is now overhead at the equator (Fig. 9), and is on the point of crossing from being north of it to south. Day and night are then equal in length, and the sun is at the so-called autumnal equinox. Since June 21 the area of the region of the midnight sun will have steadily contracted, till at Sept 23 it has become simply a point, the north pole, where the sun is for that day on the horizon throughout the twenty-four hours.

By December 21 the sun has got as far south of the equator

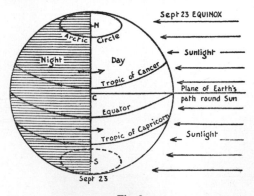

Fig. 9
The position of the Earth in relation to the incident sunlight at the time of autumnal equinox, about 23 September

as it ever gets, and this is the winter solstice. The region of the midnight sun now surrounds the south pole, and for the northern Arctic Circle the sun is perpetually below the horizon. As between the two hemispheres, the situation is the complete reverse of that of June 21.

By March 21, the sun has now moved northward again relative to the Earth and is again overhead at the equator and is about to cross from south to north. This instant is the so-called vernal equinox, or the beginning of spring.

THE DATE LINE

The day, or to give it its fuller name the *civil* day, begins at midnight when a place such as Greenwich (G-midnight) in Fig. 7 is turned as far away from the sun as possible. Twelve hours later it would be at G (noon). This circle through G and the north and south poles is called the meridian of Greenwich, and is the reference circle on the Earth from which longitudes, east and west, are measured; while latitudes are measured north and south of the equator.

If we imagine a traveller starting from London at noon on a Monday, say, and flying westwards at just over six hundred miles per hour (which is within the bounds of possibility nowadays) he would exactly offset the Earth's rotation and keep the sun always on his meridian. So it would always be noon for him. By the time he was back in London it would be noon on Tuesday, though for him there would have been no sunset. So there arises the question at what point of his journey did Monday noon change into Tuesday noon? The answer is a matter of pure convention, and it is internationally agreed that the change of date, where convenient, shall be made at the meridian directly opposite to that through Greenwich, that is in longitude 180° E or W. This line lies mainly in the Pacific Ocean, but the actual date-line, as it is called, deviates from it at a number of places in order to keep the date of certain places the same as that of other territories with which they happen to be closely associated. For instance, it deviates considerably westward to keep the Aleutian islands all on the same side of it, considerably eastward to remain over sea through the Bering Straits and so not actually across eastern Siberia, and there are other similar deviations in the southern Pacific.

When a vessel crosses this line in a westerly direction the date has to be advanced one day, but the time of day by the clock remains unchanged; and when crossing it on an easterly course, the date must be put back by a day. There is a tricky conundrum based on this: "What is the greatest possible number of Sundays one can have in February?" The obvious answer is *five*, for those particular leap years when February 1, 8, 15, 22, *and* 29 all happen to fall on Sunday. But this is not the correct answer, which in fact is *ten*. If we leave Siberia on Sunday, February 1, in one of these leap years, and sail across the Bering Strait to Alaska reaching the line just on midnight, then immediately on crossing it Sunday will just begin on the other side, and that would give us two Sundays in successive periods of twenty-four hours by the clock. We could then return during the week and repeat the performance the next week-end, and so on. If our desire for Sundays was not so intense as this, we could of course go to the other extreme and cross the other way to take full advantage of any local licensing laws. All this is nothing like so absurd as it may sound to people living on the other side of the world from the date-line and possibly never having crossed it. But during the war to my knowledge one steamer sailing from Japan to the U.S.A. first crossed the date line in the easterly direction, was then recalled and crossed it the other way, and then later still was allowed to proceed. As a result seven of their successive days on board were Wednesday, (crossed eastwards), Wednesday, Thursday, Friday, Saturday, (crossed westwards), Monday, (crossed eastwards), Monday: that is, a week with no Sunday or Tuesday, but two Mondays and two Wednesdays!

EARTH'S MAGNETIC FIELD

Everyone is aware of the fact that the Earth is magnetic, for this is how the mariner's compass works. If we are at a given place on the Earth's surface, then a small horizontal compass needle will point approximately north, but the departures from the strict north are very important. The lines along which a compass needle would point in the northern hemisphere are shown in Fig. 10, but it will be seen that they all converge to the point D, the so-called north magnetic (dip) pole. Its position is 73° N, 100° W. There is a similar diagram for the southern hemisphere, and the corresponding south magnetic pole is in position 71° S, 151° E. The line joining these two points on the Earth's surface does *not* pass through the centre, failing to do so by about seven hundred miles.

As for the strength and form of the Earth's field at points near its surface, to a fair degree of approximation it is just as though it were due to a short strong bar magnet fixed at the Earth's centre (with its poles also near the centre), though the axis of the magnet is by no means coincident with the Earth's rotation axis, but is directed towards the point 78° N, 69° W in the northern hemisphere and the diametrically opposite point 78° S, 111° E in the south: the so-called axis-poles (Fig. 11).

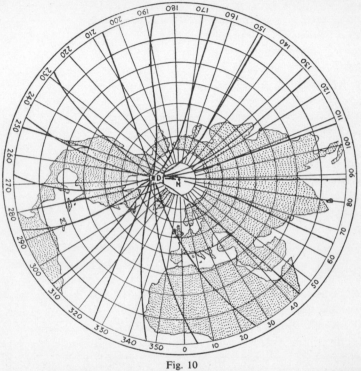

Fig. 10

Lines of horizontal magnetic force at the Earth's surface in the northern hemisphere. A horizontal compass needle points towards D and not to the true North N

It might be expected that the magnetic poles would coincide with the geographical poles, that is, the north and south poles defined by the Earth's axis of rotation, but the above values show that the places towards which the compass-needle points and the axis-poles of the main field are situated several hundred miles away from each other in each of the two hemispheres. For mariners and others relying on the compass the dip-poles have the greater importance, but from the theoretical point of view it is the axis-poles that are likely to be more significant.

It is not known for certain who first discovered the existence of the Earth's magnetic field, or its direction-finding properties by means of the compass-needle. Claims have been made that it was known to the Chinese more than four thousand years ago, and it is certain that it has been used in navigation for

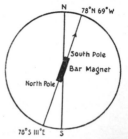

Fig. 11

The main magnetic field of the Earth is the same *as if* there were a powerful short bar-magnet at the centre, directed to the point 78°N 69°W on the Earth's surface and from the opposite point in the southern hemisphere. These are the axis-poles of the field. (The south pole of the bar-magnet is at the northerly end, and vice versa)

nearly a thousand years, but accurate and reliable recorded observations of the direction of the field at various places appear to date with certainty only from the fifteenth century. Since then, and with ever increasing attention, the Earth's field has been systematically measured and studied, but although a very great deal is known about the details and peculiarities of it, the surprising thing is that the explanation of its cause and where exactly it originates are still among the great unsolved scientific problems, despite prolonged research on the subject.

But the general mathematical theory of magnetism and electricity has been developed to a state of complete perfection as far as large scale phenomena such as ordinary magnetic fields, including of course the Earth's, are concerned, and by its means it can be proved beyond question that the field must have its origin *inside* the Earth. The external field could also be largely accounted for if the material substance of the Earth were itself uniformly magnetised at a suitable strength, but it is easily established that at least the near surface layers are not magnetised up to the necessary strength, indeed for the most part not to any appreciable extent whatever. Also, owing to the gradual rise of temperature with depth, it seems unlikely that the material lower down can be magnetisable at all in any permanent form. On the other hand the field could be due to some system of electric currents flowing round within the

Earth, but unless these were in some way maintained by the steady supply of power they would undoubtedly decay. Thus the problem of the cause of the Earth's magnetic field brings us again to the necessity for knowing something of its inner structure, what it is made of, and the condition its materials may be in at the various depths.

THE INTERIOR OF THE EARTH

But here we come up against a great difficulty. The deepest borings yet made into the Earth only go down a mile or two, so weak are the forces and resources at the disposal of man compared with those of Nature that he is trying to contend with,

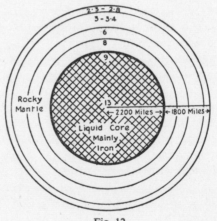

Fig. 12
A cross-section through the centre of the Earth.
The density increases downwards from about
2·3 near the surface to about 13 at the centre.
(Water = 1)

and evidence from such borings sheds no light whatever on this magnetic problem. What we really need to know is the structure of the Earth hundreds and even thousands of miles below the surface, in fact the structure right down to the centre almost four thousand miles below the surface.

Now once again Nature has been kind to us and a fortunate

thing happens in the phenomenon of earthquakes—that is, fortunate for those interested in these problems, but not so for those who happen to live near where they occur. It turns out that detailed study of earthquakes enables the general picture of the whole internal structure of the Earth and the prevailing conditions deep down below the surface to be inferred.

For simplicity, let us reverse the actual procedure and describe first what the interior is now known to be like, and then with this clear before us explain how it has been inferred by means of earthquakes. Fig. 12 shows a cross-section through the Earth's centre. There is first an upper layer about ten miles deep, but varying in thickness somewhat from place to place; a somewhat deeper and denser intermediate layer; and then a far deeper layer of still denser material extending to a depth of eighteen hundred miles below the outer surface. The density of the material increases as we go downwards mainly as a result of the sheer weight of the overlying material which compresses the rocks lying beneath. The numerical values of the density, as compared with that of water ($=1$), are shown at a number of depths in Fig. 12. This rocky shell or mantle, as it is called, is perfectly firm and stiff, and has a rigidity comparable with that of steel, but it is composed entirely of rock.

With our direct knowledge of the composition of the outer layers, all this is reasonable enough and perhaps to be expected, but at the bottom of this shell, 1800 miles down, a most extraordinary change occurs. The central region, 4400 miles across, is actually a great molten core of heavy metals, mainly iron, but containing also some nickel and possibly similar metals. It is at high temperature, several thousand degrees, since this is what is needed to maintain the metals in liquid form. The material is also compressed by the pressure of the overlying layers, and at the centre is at least fifty per cent more dense than it would be if uncompressed.

Now how is all this ascertained from earthquakes? When an earthquake occurs it is as though something at least as powerful as an atomic bomb had been let off deep below the surface. Great devastation may occur locally in the regions more or less directly above the disturbance, but what is of importance for the present purpose is that the general shock also sends out waves of vibration into the body of the Earth, just as an explosion sends out sound waves into the atmosphere far beyond the locality where it happens. The waves in and under the ground spread out for hundreds and even thousands of miles round the centre of the disturbance. A large earthquake can shake the whole planet right through to its very centre and out to the furthest parts of the surface. At great distances, these waves on coming to the surface are felt as slight ground tremors, and their arrivals can be recorded by delicate automatic instruments, called seismographs, that are always in readiness for the purpose at innumerable stations in many parts of the world.

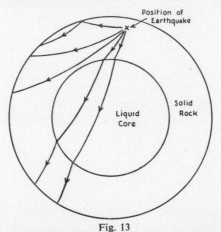

Fig. 13

Typical paths of seismic rays emanating from an earthquake. The rays are refracted at the interface between the rocky mantle and liquid core. They bend upwards because of the increasing density with greater depth

If the Earth were made of the same uniform material everywhere, the paths of these waves would be straight lines, but in fact the actual paths are found to be curved upwards, as shown in Fig. 13. Some waves that penetrate as far as the core are reflected off its surface, and others pass through the core to emerge on the far side. The fact that the waves in the outer mantle are always bent upwards shows that if the material is everywhere of much the same composition, then it must become denser with increasing depth. In this way the waves reveal the effect of compression.

Now the theory of the motion of waves in solids and liquids is well understood, and the waves that reach a given place on the Earth's surface are of two main kinds. First, there are what are termed Push-waves, or P-waves. In any wave-motion the particles of the material do not move bodily through any finite distance but merely vibrate by very small amounts about the places they would occupy if there were no waves. Now in

Fig. 14

The propagation of Push-waves.

The oscillation of the particle at P is limited to a very short range P'P", and the same holds for every other particle of matter. The particle moves to and fro in the line P'PP", along the ray in which the wave travels, and this sets in motion the adjacent particle at Q, and so on

P-waves, this oscillation is in the same direction as the waves travel. In Fig. 14 is shown how the material particles move to and fro along the ray itself to create a P-wave. These Push-waves can be transmitted through solid material, such as that of the rocky mantle, and also through liquid material, such as that in the core.

Second, however, are the so-called Shake-waves or S-waves. The waves themselves still travel along similar paths to the P-waves, but now the vibrations of the elements of the material are sideways, or transverse to the rays along which the waves themselves travel. This is illustrated in Fig. 15. And here now is the feature that reveals the liquid nature of the core: these Shake-waves can only be transmitted through rigid solid material, and not at all through liquid. This is more or less obvious physically; for if in Fig. 14 we consider a near element of material at Q, the vibrations of P must affect the material at Q simply by "pushing" it forwards irrespective of whether the material is in the solid or liquid state. But in Fig. 15 rapid sideways vibrations at P will not be communicated to Q unless the material has some degree of rigidity. If it is liquid, P can

vibrate sideways without immediately affecting Q. What is
found from the study of earthquake waves is that no waves of
this second kind, that is no Shake-waves, are ever found to pass
through the central core, though in the rigid mantle they go
right up to its surface. This is how it is known that the core is
liquid.

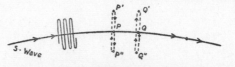

Fig. 15
The propagation of S-waves.
The vibrations of an element P are now sideways in a very small range P'P". The particle
oscillates in the line P'PP", as indicated by
the arrows. P will set Q in sideways motion
only in rigid material, not in liquid

We are still discussing the subject in the reverse order to that
actually carried out, and the next question is accordingly how
these various waves are identified. Now the speeds of the various
waves are found to range from about two and a half miles per
second for the slowest up to about eight miles per second for
the fastest—these correspond to the speed of sound in the
materials concerned (in ordinary air this speed is about one
fifth of a mile per second). The speeds and the forms of the
paths depend on the composition of the material they are
going through and on its degree of compression, that is its
density; and it is this feature of earthquake paths that enables
even the materials to be identified.

At this point another piece of good fortune enters. It always
happens for every material that the Push-waves travel faster
than the Shake-waves—anything from about fifty to ninety
per cent faster according to the material, and so at any recording
station the P-waves invariably arrive first from a given earthquake to be followed several seconds or even minutes later by
the S-waves.

Fig. 16 shows a drawing of a typical seismographic earthquake record. The left of the record is before any waves arrive,
then suddenly come the P-waves, to be followed in this case

about twenty seconds later by the Shake-waves. Now time differences of this kind are being measured at stations all over the world, and though neither the instant of occurrence nor the place of origin itself will in general be known, records at two or three stations sufficiently far apart suffice to locate it even though it may have taken place in some remote region such as far beneath the ocean bed on the other side of the world.

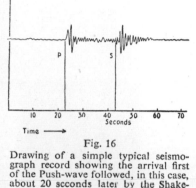

Time ⟶

Fig. 16

Drawing of a simple typical seismograph record showing the arrival first of the Push-wave followed, in this case, about 20 seconds later by the Shake-wave

The actual process of finding the structure has been a long and intricate one, but in brief it consists of postulating a certain internal distribution of the Earth, and working out the travel-times that theoretical earthquake waves in it would take between definite selected starting points and places at the surface. These give theoretical time differences for P- and S-waves which are then compared with the previous measured time-differences, and the degree of agreement or disagreement found. By gradually adjusting the assumed internal structure, the differences between the theoretical values and the recorded values are reduced to a point where no further improvement is possible and the outstanding differences attributable solely to small random influences. It is in this way that the internal structure of the Earth has been gradually inferred with ever increasing detail and accuracy over the past fifty years.

The observed effects are complicated, and as well as straight-forward direct waves other waves arrive that have been both reflected and refracted at various interfaces between layers deep down in the Earth. The uppermost layer has wave-properties similar to granite, the next one is identifiable with basalt, while the lowest layer of the mantle resembles the densest rocks that are found at the surface through having been erupted from far below. The liquid core itself is composed mainly of molten iron. The general composition of the whole Earth in terms of these substances is roughly as follows:

Molten iron . . .	35·0%
Dense rock . . .	64·6%
Granite . . .	0·36%
Sedimentary rock . .	0·016%
Oceans . . .	0·024%

As this table suggests, the Earth is largely made up of the so-called heavy elements, that is those of high atomic weight. For astronomical purposes the whole of the ninety-two elements divide naturally into two groups: in the first of these come the light elements, hydrogen (H) and helium (He), which are enormously abundant in the stars, particularly hydrogen, which comprises at least ninety per cent of the sun's whole mass and is also very abundant in interstellar space, and indeed throughout the universe, as we shall see in the sequel. In the second group, for reasons that will appear later, are to be included all the other elements, such as iron, silicon, oxygen, etc., which are usually referred to collectively as the heavy elements, even though the lightest of them are not much heavier than helium.

It is not possible to transform the above table accurately into percentage-contents of the Earth by elements, though it is nevertheless immediately clear from it that heavy elements make up by far the greater part, and that hydrogen and helium must contribute very little. But the composition of the extreme outer layers, say within a few miles of the surface, has however been determined simply by analysis of a large number of typical representative rocks, and it is found that these principal *heavy* elements go to make up at least 99 per cent of the total weight, while all the heavy elements make up nearly 99·9 per cent. The following table shows these percentages in detail and refers to about one three-hundredth part of the Earth's total mass comprised by its outer layers:

	%			%
Oxygen	46·4	Sodium	. .	2·8
Silicon	27·6	Potassium	. .	2·6
Aluminium	8·1	Magnesium	.	2·1
Iron	5·1	Titanium	. .	0·7
Calcium	3·6	All others	. .	0·9
		Hydrogen	. .	0·13

Clearly this information must be of special importance when it comes to the consideration of possible sources for the origin of the Earth. It would be no use, for example, simply to suppose that the Earth had been lifted bodily out of the sun, as several early theories such as the tidal and collision hypotheses did, because obviously such an Earth instead of consisting largely of heavy elements would have quite the wrong composition and be formed mainly of hydrogen. It is now known that there are other grave objections to these early theories, the most important perhaps being the dynamical difficulty of getting planets formed from the sun to circle it at the great distances that the real planets in fact move at. It might be possible by means of the effect of a passing star to extract planets from the sun (regardless of composition) that subsequently moved round it more or less skimming the surface, but the mighty Jupiter which weighs far more than all the other planets put together moves at about one thousand solar radii from the sun, and no one has ever suggested a process whereby such a body could be ejected from the sun and got into a path at all comparable with its present one. The high hydrogen contents of the sun and stars have come to be clearly recognised only comparatively recently, whereas the dynamical objection to a solar origin for the Earth and planets was appreciated at an earlier stage. It had already caused astronomers to look elsewhere than to the sun for a possible source of the planetary material, and the solution that suggested itself was that of another star, perhaps a former companion to the sun, already moving at a distance from the sun comparable with those of the great planets now. Any process such as tidal action by another star, that had hitherto been invoked to remove material from the sun would be equally applicable to the companion star, and thus would get over the difficulty posed by the enormous range of the planetary system compared with the size of the sun. But the composition difficulty would remain, since we now know that it would not be reasonable to postulate a companion star to the sun consisting largely of heavy elements. We shall see in a later chapter the significance of this composition difficulty and how it may be surmounted.

THE ORIGIN OF THE MAGNETIC FIELD?

Let us then come back to the starting point of this discussion of the Earth's interior, namely the origin of the magnetic field. It is now generally agreed by those actively engaged on this difficult problem that the cause must be assigned to the liquid core of the Earth. The reasons for this are fairly simple; accumulated detailed measurements have gradually established that the field is subject to all sorts of changes of both regular and irregular kinds, and seems to move about slowly inside the Earth. For example, as one of the main changes, the axis-poles although not changing in latitude show a progressive movement in longitude. The northern pole appears to be moving westwards at a rate of about four or five degrees of longitude per century, with a corresponding movement of the diametrically opposite southern axis-pole. Moreover the general strength of the field seems to have diminished by about five per cent during the past century.

Now if the field were set in the solid rocky outer mantle, it could scarcely move about within the Earth or change much at all, quite apart from whether it could in fact be located there because of temperature effects. But the core itself is at even higher temperature and there is no possibility whatever of any permanent static magnetism existing in molten iron. For this reason it is concluded that magnetism can only be produced in the core if some sort of movements, that is actual mass-motions, occur in the liquid in it, over and above any general steady

rotation with the Earth that the core as a whole will almost
certainly have. The kind of movements needed would be a
general flow in meridian planes (Fig. 17). It can be shown
that such a motion of the molten liquid iron taken in conjunction with the magnetic field itself would be able by

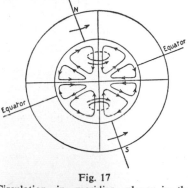

Fig. 17

Circulation in meridian planes in the
Earth's core. This is the kind of motion
which, if somehow forced to continue,
could maintain a magnetic field

induction to produce electromotive forces that could balance
out the resistance losses. But some cause would be needed to
maintain the slow circulation of the liquid in accordance with
some such scheme as that illustrated in Fig. 17. So there are two
aspects to the problem: the first is to decide what possible
systems of circulatory currents within the core would produce
the observed magnetic field, and this part has been tackled with
a fair measure of success in recent years.

There remains however the second aspect, namely what
could cause the liquid in this core to circulate round, in prefer-
ence to just staying where it is and keeping still apart from its
general rotation with the Earth as a whole. Now, although it
may not be the only possible process, one of the most hopeful
means of accounting for this depends on a part of the rotation
of the Earth itself, that we actually glossed over when we were
dealing with this matter earlier in this chapter, but which we
must now go into in more detail.

PRECESSION OF THE EARTH'S AXIS

Earlier on it was said that as the Earth moves round the sun in its annual journey, the axis of rotation points always in a fixed direction (near to the star Polaris), but in reality this is not strictly true, and in fact it slowly describes a kind of cone in a backwards direction, as shown in Fig. 18. If for the moment

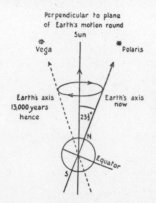

Fig. 18

Diagram showing how the Earth's axis precesses. It describes a cone of semi-angle $23\frac{1}{2}°$ round the line perpendicular to the plane of motion. (The centre of the Earth moves round the sun once a year independently of this motion.) The precession takes 26,000 years to describe the cone, so in 13,000 years the Earth is tipped over by 47° through this cause, and back round again in another 13,000 years

we think of the centre of the Earth as fixed, then the axis of rotation, the north-south axis, gradually moves round to sweep out a cone; the motion is quite independent of the yearly motion of the Earth round the sun. By ordinary standards the rate is very slow, taking nearly 26,000 years to go once round the cone. If we think of it in terms of the point in the heavens towards which the axis points, at the moment this as stated is almost towards the bright star Polaris, but 13,000 years ago and 13,000 years hence it will be roughly towards the present position of the bright star Vega, (a Lyrae), as shown in Fig. 19. The angle at which the axis slopes over away from the direction perpendicular to the general plane of motion of the Earth round the Sun is $23\frac{1}{2}$ degrees.

Accordingly this motion of precession turns the whole Earth over through 47° in a mere 13,000 years. This may at first sight seem a very slow and unimportant change, but astronomically it is extremely rapid, and if one reflects how large the Earth is and how quickly it is rotating, one soon realises that it must require prodigious forces to shift the Earth in this way. It means that at the Earth's surface the north pole (fixed in the Earth) is moving about ten feet a day. There is no doubt whatever about the existence of the motion, for it can readily be seen from year to year, and was easily discovered by the ancients even though they had no telescopes to help them. It has a rather splendid

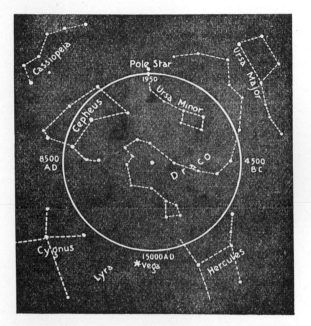

Fig. 19

The path in the sky followed by the direction of the Earth's axis. At present it points nearly to the Pole star (Polaris). It will gradually move on through the constellation of Cepheus and in 13,000 years' time the "north star" will be near Vega (α Lyrae), while in 26,000 years it will be round near the present north-star Polaris again

name in astronomy, "the precession of the equinoxes," for the reason that its effect is to alter progressively the instants at which the Sun crosses through the plane of the Earth's equator, from south to north at spring and from north to south at autumn, that is the "equinoxes," and cause them to "precede" the expected time. But careful allowance for this motion is made in settling the length of the day and the appropriate length of the year.

The forces that produce the motion arise because the Earth is not perfectly spherical but, as we have already explained, flattened at the polar regions and broadened out at the equatorial parts, and also because the Earth's axis of figure, the north-south axis, is inclined over at this angle of 23½ degrees. The attractions of the sun and moon, besides keeping the

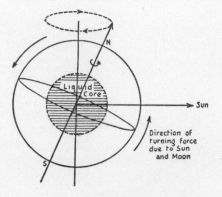

Fig. 20
Showing the couple, or twist, due to the attraction of the moon and sun on the non-spherical Earth. This causes the solid outer mantle to precess, and the liquid core has to adjust itself to this motion

various bodies moving round each other, produce also a couple (or twisting force) on the Earth just because of these two features—the non-spherical shape and the sloping-over axis (Fig. 20). The direction of this couple, or twist, is such as to try to bring the Earth's axis into the upright position, but because of the gyroscopic effect of the rapid spin of the Earth no such direct response is dynamically possible, and instead the axis describes this cone. However, the average place of the axis, namely the axis of the cone itself, is where the sun and moon are trying to force it to be. But in fact the Earth yields nothing to them and maintains the inclination of its axis unchanged throughout at this value of 23½ degrees.

All this is a matter of dynamics and is well understood

today, but it took no less a person than Newton himself to supply the correct theoretical explanation for the first time. The situation is exactly the same as with the familiar spinning top when this slopes over instead of being upright, and the motion of a top will be familiar to everybody without going into the theory of the thing. Fig. 21 shows the well-known motion

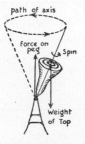

path of axis

force on peg   Spin

Weight of Top

Fig. 21

Motion of a spinning top with fixed peg. The couple or twisting force is due to the upward reaction on the peg and the downward weight of the top. Here it is the opposite way from the couple on the Earth, and so the precession of the top is *forwards* as indicated

of a top, which is also called "precession" from analogy with this motion of the axis of the spinning Earth. But in the case of the top the twisting couple is caused by its own weight and the equal upward reaction of the peg. It is trying to turn the top away from the upright position, and as a result the direction of the precession is the opposite way from that of the Earth.

Now keeping this motion in mind, how is this great sphere of liquid metal that forms the Earth's core going to react when the vessel containing it, namely the rigid outer mantle of the Earth, is whisked round in this rapid manner? Remember when liquid is inside a vessel, it is by no means rigidly attached to it even though it entirely fills it. The only condition that the liquid has to fulfil is that very near the inner surface of the container the motion of the liquid must be the same as that of the solid surface.

It need scarcely be said that it is an intricate mathematical problem to discover what motion is set up in the core, but it can in fact be proved that in order to accommodate itself to the precessional motion, the core must set up circulation and other motions within itself. The precession is permanently forced upon the Earth by the actions of the sun and moon, and accordingly there is a source of energy to maintain these circulation currents deep down in the central core of the Earth.

And it is along such lines as these that there seems to be hope that the problem of the Earth's magnetism will eventually be solved.

It must be emphasized that the matter is by no means settled yet; what has been outlined above constitutes little more than the first steps with a very difficult problem. But I have brought up this subject in order to give some idea how intimately related these various objects, the Earth, moon, and sun, must be regarded as being. At first sight it might seem out of the question that the magnetism deep down in the centre of the Earth could be anything to do with the presence of the sun and moon, yet all this goes to show that it may well be so, and it serves to illustrate how carefully all possible effects must be examined if we are going to get to the root of a complex problem.

REFERENCES

The Age of the Earth, A. Holmes, Nelson, 1937.

The Earth's Magnetism, S. Chapman, Methuen, 1936.

The Solar System and Its Origin, H. N. Russell, Macmillan, 1935.

The Interior of the Earth, E. C. Bullard, see *The Earth as a Planet*, University of Chicago Press, 1953.

The Earth, H. Jeffreys, Cambridge University Press, 1952.

"The Effect of Precession on the Motion of the Earth's Liquid Core," H. Bondi and R. A. Lyttleton, *Proceedings of the Cambridge Philosophical Society*, 1953.

II

THE MOON

Nearest neighbour—Possibility of man reaching moon—Earth's atmosphere—Auroral clouds—Artificial satellites — Phases — Eclipses — Tidal friction—Slowing down of Earth's rotation—Lunar surface—Seas—Same face always towards Earth—Librations—Craters—Effective distance telescopically—No surface changes detected—Cause of craters—Volcanic hypothesis not tenable—Meteoritic impacts—Explosions so caused more violent than atom bombs—Buried craters—Deep dust layers—Dust as shallow atmosphere—Craters on the Earth?—Air resistance—Meteorites found—Erosion of craters by weather—Arizona crater—Chubb crater—Siberian meteorite—Larger craters on Earth?—Conditions on moon.

REACHING THE MOON

The moon is our nearest neighbour in space; its average distance from the Earth is about 240,000 miles. Next to the sun, the moon is of special importance to us, and has played a fundamental part in the development of astronomy. Through its close proximity and rapid motion, the moon provides a rigorous test of the law of gravitation, while study of the tides and of eclipses has also produced many important advances, and not least the question of the formation of the Earth-moon system has stimulated much research.

The possibility of man being able to reach the moon is now being seriously discussed, and although it would be difficult to say whether a journey to the moon with any chance of survival will be made some years hence by anyone alive today, it may very well be that a small projectile of some sort will be successfully propelled right out of the Earth's gravitational attraction within the next few decades. Once this can be achieved, the next step will be to project it in such a way that it lands on the moon, but it would be a much greater step still to project an object capable of also performing the return journey, even if only a small part of itself is to make this return. So the first passenger journeys to the moon will have one-way tickets only, though it need not be supposed that this will deter volunteers altogether. Thirty years or so ago there was a popular craze for going over Niagara Falls in a barrel, and one learns that there was no lack of sufficiently intrepid persons willing to risk their life on an enterprise that may have had an element of notoriety about it, but was without any important enrichment of mankind resulting. So possibly in another thirty years' time, there may be a similar craze with a steady supply of volunteers for a journey to the moon. But as we shall see there will be many more dangers to contend with than in the few hundred feet drop of the barrel-occupants.

Let us consider what such a journey would involve if we could in fact make it without risk. Rockets have already been sent up successfully 100 miles or more above the Earth's surface, and cameras recovered from these show what our own Earth would look like to a passenger in such a rocket.

THE EARTH'S ATMOSPHERE

As we go upwards through the Earth's atmosphere it becomes more and more rarefied; by the time we are ten miles up about 90 per cent of the atmosphere is behind us; twenty miles up about 99 per cent is below us, and so on. Curiously enough, however, the temperature although falling to begin with soon starts to increase again, and at great heights is well over a thousand degrees (Fig. 22). But one would not get any sensation of warmth from it at these great heights because the air is so rarefied that the amount of heat it could bring to any object surrounded by it would be very small.

Between about fifteen and twenty miles up there is spread a layer of ozone (ozone is a special form of oxygen), which has extremely important effects. If all this ozone were brought down to ground level, that is to normal temperature and pressure, it would make a layer only a tenth of an inch deep, but this small amount is as opaque to the sun's ultra-violet light as would be six feet of lead. This is one of the reasons why the study of these high atmospheric levels is of such interest today because they are likely to provide the key to many of the details of the sun's light.

It is not yet known how far upwards our atmosphere extends. Faintly luminous clouds can often be seen fifty or sixty miles up, while auroral clouds are seen at anything from 60 to even 600 miles up. These aurorae, or northern lights, are often brilliantly red or green clouds, looking like gossamer curtains hanging in the sky. The particles producing them come in mainly towards the magnetic poles, and the light of the aurorae is due mainly to their collision with the upper atmosphere. At the present time this high atmosphere can only be studied indirectly, and results so derived therefore have some degree of uncertainty. This is why scientific importance attaches to the proposed artificial satellites that we read so much about nowadays. If these can be launched into the high atmosphere a few hundred miles up they will be able to carry instruments that may be able to radio back information as to many of the prevailing conditions.

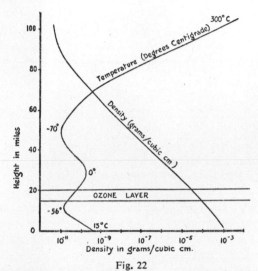

Fig. 22

Graphs showing how the density and temperature in the Earth's atmosphere change to a height of about 100 miles. The ozone-layer is confined mainly between 15 and 20 miles high

ARTIFICIAL SATELLITES

If a satellite is to travel round the Earth and keep at the same height of, say, three hundred miles above the surface, what will need to be done is first to carry the satellite up to this height by rocket and then set it moving horizontally, that is parallel to the ground, with an appropriate speed (Fig. 23). The requisite speed is 17,000 miles an hour, and if it is given just this velocity it will carry on always at the same height, in a circle round the Earth without further aid, and do the whole circuit in about one and a half hours. If the speed appreciably falls short of this rate, the satellite would immediately begin to lose height and eventually fall to the ground. If the speed were greater, the effect would be such as to carry it out further on the opposite side of the Earth, and a certain amount of this would not matter because then the satellite would be moving at different heights

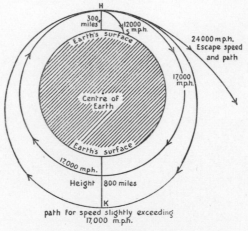

Fig. 23

Trajectories of an artificial satellite.

Tl e satellite must first be carried up to a point H and then projected horizontally at 17,000 m.p.h. If the speed is less than this the satellite would fall and strike the ground at S. If it is greater, the path will carry it out further to K on the opposite side of the Earth and during the motion the height will vary. If the speed reaches or exceeds 24,000 m.p.h. the satellite will escape altogether from the Earth and never return. (The height scale is exaggerated)

at different parts of its path, which would probably be an advantage in allowing conditions at different heights to be found. But if the speed exceeded 24,000 miles per hour the satellite would fly off altogether never to return. This is the initial speed that would be needed to project something to the moon, which will presumably be the next step in the business, but it is going to be difficult enough to achieve the 17,000 miles per hour, one would imagine.

American and Russian scientists evidently believe they will be able to do this within the next few years, and no doubt competition is going on to see who can manage it first. But whoever wins Nature has beaten them both to it and already launched a satellite a quarter of a million miles up for us in the shape of the moon.

PHASES OF THE MOON

The moon goes round the Earth in $27\frac{1}{3}$ days and overtakes the sun, which can be regarded as going round the Earth, every

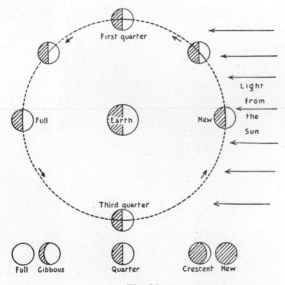

Fig. 24

The phases of the moon. The sunlight, shown as coming from the right, illuminates only that half of the moon presented to the sun. The observer on the Earth can see practically none of this part at new moon, but then the amount gradually increases till it is all visible at full moon, after which it decreases again. The corresponding phases as seen from Earth between new and full moon are shown at the bottom of the diagram

$29\frac{1}{2}$ days. When the moon as seen from the Earth is in the same direction as the sun, it is said to be *new*, and then as it moves round it proceeds to go through all its phases. A week later it is at first quarter and we on Earth see a half-moon. A second week later the moon is directly opposite the sun, and is *full*. A week later still it is at third quarter and again we see a half-moon. Then it decreases almost to invisibility before becoming new again (Fig. 24).

SOLAR ECLIPSES

By a curious piece of good fortune the moon is just about the right size to eclipse the sun and blot out its blinding light, thereby enabling us to observe what actually surrounds the sun

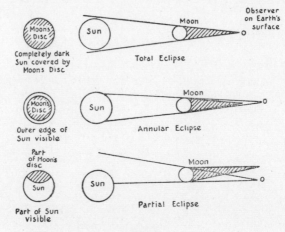

Fig. 25
Configuration of sun and moon relative to an observer O on
the Earth for total, annular, and partial eclipses.
On the left is shown the appearance of the sun in each case

outside the circular boundary that we normally see, and it also allows us even to see the stars that appear to lie near its edge, but which in fact of course are millions of times further away.

The moon weighs about $\frac{1}{81}$ of the Earth, and is only about a quarter of its radius, with the result that gravity on the surface of the moon is only about one sixth of what it is here on Earth. As a result a cricketer could throw a ball nearly half a mile, and the high jump record on the moon would be about twenty feet. It is precisely because of this smaller gravity that the moon has no detectable atmosphere of any kind; it simply has not the attractive force to hold one. The edge of the moon therefore gives a sharp well-defined shadow on the opposite side from the sun and produces a narrow cone of complete darkness. The sharp tip or vertex of this cone may on occasion come slightly above the Earth's surface and the moon is then not quite near enough to us to cover the sun's disc (Fig. 25). If we were at the right part of the Earth's surface the whole outer edge of the sun would remain visible, showing a brilliant ring or annulus. This is called an annular eclipse, but the more important eclipses are when this cone reaches down below the Earth's surface so that places on it are in actual darkness. Then the area of total eclipse can be anything up to about 160 miles across when the sun is more or less overhead. The region of darkness made by the shadow of the moon travels across the Earth's surface at a speed between 1000 and 4000 miles per hour, following a complicated path which is settled not only by the moon's motion but by the rotation of the Earth. Under the most favourable conditions the time for which the sun is completely eclipsed at any one place, totality, as it is called, can last about $7\frac{1}{2}$ minutes. Annular eclipses can last as long as about $12\frac{1}{2}$ minutes, but usually they are much shorter than this. There must always be somewhere on the Earth at least two eclipses of the sun (partial, total, or annular) every year; there are usually four; and sometimes five. The region on the Earth where an eclipse is partial may cover a track thousands of miles wide, and so at any given place partial eclipses occur more frequently than total eclipses.

Although the number of eclipses is quite large, it is extremely rare for there to be a total eclipse at any given place. The reason for this is that the central band where totality can happen is so very narrow, and if one waited at a given place for a total eclipse there would be one on the average only once every 360 years or so, though at quite irregular times. The last total eclipse visible somewhere in England was on 29 June 1927 when the central shadow band cut across the north of England. The precise path of the shadow and the time of duration of eclipses can be worked out years in advance with an accuracy within a matter of seconds at most. It is the success of predictions of this kind that

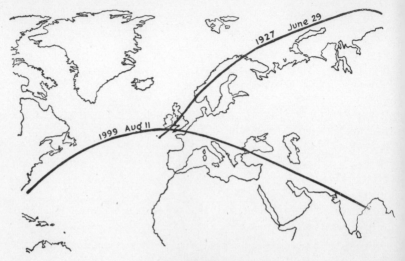

Fig. 26

The two eclipse tracks that cross England during the present century, 29 June 1927, and 11 August 1999. The heavy line is the path of totality. The latter track is expected just to cross the foot of Cornwall

shows that both theory and facts concerning the solar system are completely reliable. The next total eclipse of the sun visible somewhere in England will be on 11 August 1999, when the shadow of the moon will sweep across the foot of Cornwall (Fig. 26).

TIDAL FRICTION

The moon is also mainly responsible for the tides on the Earth, with the sun also assisting, simply by its direct attraction on the water. The rotation of the Earth carries the tidal bulges forwards, and then the back attraction of the water in them upon the moon urges it forward in its motion (Fig. 27). This is having the effect of driving the moon very slowly away from the Earth, and to compensate within the system the rotation of the

Earth is actually slowing down. The day is therefore getting steadily longer, but the increase amounts to no more than a thousandth of a second in a century.

Small as this change may seem, it nevertheless requires braking action working continuously at two thousand million

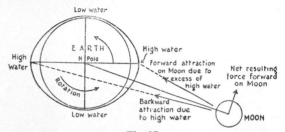

Fig. 27

The attraction of the moon (and sun) causes high water at opposite parts of the Earth's surface. The daily rotation tends to carry these tidal bulges forwards ahead of the moon, and the combined effect of their attraction is then to urge the moon forwards in its path and cause it to recede (very slowly) from the Earth.

The angle by which the tide is carried forward is very small for the open oceans, but in shallow narrow seas running north and south a large delay can occur giving an appreciable effect

horse-power to slow up the rotation of the Earth. The necessary action occurs mainly in the Bering Sea, south of Alaska and Siberia, where there is a wide expanse of fast running shallow water moving mainly north and south with the tides. Small as it is, this rate of retardation is in any case just about as large as is allowable considering the great age of the Earth. For if we think of the process going backwards in time, the day must once have been much shorter and the moon correspondingly nearer, and there must obviously be a limit beyond which the process cannot have taken the system in the past without the moon and the Earth coming into collision.

SURFACE APPEARANCE

At the time of the full moon, the sun is behind us in the opposite direction and shining directly down on the lunar surface. A number of features are immediately obvious, such as the very different degrees of brightness at different parts of the surface. Some parts are as brilliant as if they were of white sand, and other parts look as dark as would slate. But we cannot infer any such immediate identification, because there may be a whole host of substances that would do equally well. Also, conditions at the moon's surface are so different from those on Earth that it would be hazardous to suppose even that the same substance would have the same colour and appearance at the two places. Also there are questions of aspect: even the same area of the moon does not look the same when viewed from different angles, as the intricate motion of the moon happens to make it possible for us to do.

The large dark areas, more or less circular in shape, are called "seas," but it must be emphasised that this is only a name carried on from an even less knowledgeable age than our own, and that they are *not* seas of water. There is no water-vapour or water of any kind on the moon. What we are seeing when we look at it is a completely arid ball of rock 2,160 miles in diameter.

Although there is no water or any other mobile liquid on the moon's surface, the gravitational attraction of the Earth nevertheless produces tidal effects in the actual material body of the satellite. The shape is slightly deformed by the action of the Earth to produce a bodily-tide, and the resulting effect on the moon has been very much greater in slowing it up than the reverse effects have been in retarding the Earth. This is of course mainly because of the Earth's far greater mass. If the moon were turning right round as viewed from the Earth, clearly the tidal bulges would be carried away from the places on the moon's surface immediately under and opposite the Earth, and there would result a similar braking effect to that already explained to occur for the lunar tides in our oceans. And this has in fact already slowed up the moon's rotation to such an extent that it always turns the same face towards the Earth. The moon has come to be extremely well-mannered in this and never turns her back on the assembled company. So we never see the back of the moon.

The moon itself rotates at an absolutely constant rate, taking 27 days 7 hours 43 minutes $11\frac{1}{2}$ seconds to turn round once, exactly the same time as it takes to go once round the Earth. This latter motion, however, does not occur always at the same rate because the moon's path is not exactly a circle but an ellipse with the Earth at one of the focal points. We therefore can see alternately a few degrees (not quite 8°) further round the eastern edge and then later on round the western edge. Similarly, the moon's path round the Earth is inclined at a few degrees (just over 6°) to the moon's equator, so that at one part of the month the north-pole of the moon is tipped over about six degrees towards us while a fortnight later the south-pole is similarly inclined over towards the Earth. Also, as the Earth rotates we see the moon first when it rises a little from one side and then are carried across (at the equator nearly 8000 miles) to see it with ourselves a little displaced to the other side. All these effects are called geometrical librations, and their combined result is that in fact about 59 per cent of the lunar surface can be seen: about 41 per cent (covering six million square miles) is always visible; regions amounting to 18 per cent are sometimes visible and sometimes invisible; and about 41 per cent—the back of the moon—is never visible.

When viewed with the unaided eye it is the vague details of the dark seas and lighter areas of this 41 per cent always presented towards the Earth that give the "Man-in-the-moon" his face. But with the least magnification any resemblance to a face becomes evanescent. In a large telescope are seen a host of far smaller details. Many of the larger surface features can easily be seen with ordinary field-glasses, such as the dark seas and some of the larger craters, particularly the brilliant one Tycho, well to the south, with bright rays or streaks radiating from it.

But with the glare of the full moon coming straight back at us is not the best time to study the details. When the moon is about a week old the sun is away to the right and only the right-hand half (for people in northerly latitudes) is visible. The moon is now at first quarter, and although it then sends in all only about one-seventh as much light as the full-moon, the shadows thrown by the surface features bring out the relief very much better, rather like having a reading lamp in the right place. At third-quarter the total light is only about one-ninth that of the full-moon, because of the darker areas on that half. The boundary of the shadow, the so-called terminator, is seen to be very irregular; this is because the moon's visible surface is very mountainous, a large proportion of it being corrugated by innumerable craters. Their walls run up thousands of feet in height, and it is the dark shadows of these that for the most part produce the irregular effect at the terminator. The craters give an illusion of great depth, but have in fact very flat saucer-like shapes.

The most obvious features of the lunar surface are perhaps the seas, which may very likely themselves be the remains of extremely large craters, and the craters which range in size from the smallest visible up to some hundred miles or more across. Typical lunar craters are circular, though they may appear elliptical when they are not near the centre of the moon's disc and we are not looking straight down on them. The surrounding ring forming the boundary of a large crater may have a height up to about 20,000 feet above the level of the crater floor and about 5000 feet above the general level of the surrounding lunar surface. The floor within the craters is sometimes deep and irregular, and frequently in the centre of them is a moderately high peak resembling a mountain, but the summit of the peak is always below the lunar surface outside the crater. Many craters appear to be filled nearly to their brims and have perfectly level floors. At certain regions the craters are extraordinarily numerous, and new well-defined craters encroach on presumably older less well-defined ones. Often, the wall of a larger crater is broken into at many points by newer smaller ones, and in some places the surface is a complete chaos of craters of all sizes. Careful examination of the seemingly smooth seas shows a number of formations that can only be interpreted as the rims of craters protruding out of them, and many smaller craters are to be found in the seas, though far fewer in a given area than elsewhere.

There are also to be seen a few long lines of cliffs, but of only moderate height, which may be the result of upward and downward displacement along a crack in the surface layer, but not eroded down as are similar features on the Earth. There are also many irregular deep narrow valleys, termed rills, and numberless straight clefts less than a mile across but running hundreds of miles right through all the intervening irregularities of surface. And there are the strange bright streaks, some ten miles or so broad, that extend out from many of the craters but have no perceptible shadow effects and must presumably be an extremely thin superficial phenomenon. They also run right across all other irregularities without any resulting change in colour or width. The most distinctive of them surround the great crater Tycho in the southern hemisphere, but there are numerous other examples.

NO DETECTABLE CHANGES

The "geography" of the Moon is called *selenography*. Each and every visible crater, formation, and region has been carefully charted and named, mainly by classical names, but these having proved insufficient the names of astronomers have also been brought into service. It has sometimes been said that the surface of the moon is better known than that of the Earth, and this may still be true apart of course from the back. There are something like two hundred thousand craters visible in all.

With the most powerful modern astronomical instruments the moon is effectively brought within something like fifty miles of the Earth, as far as mere magnification is concerned. Theoretically, well-defined objects rather less than one hundred yards across ought to be distinguishable, but in practice the actual degree of detail visible is never as fine as this, mainly because of the ever-present terrestrial atmosphere which always lies between us and any celestial object. Indeed, when it comes to the resolution of small detail, it is doubtful if with any equipment even under the best seeing conditions the moon could be brought nearer than about five hundred miles, though of course as aforesaid the magnification of large features corresponds to much closer distances. Despite this limitation we can be practically certain that no real detectable changes have occurred on the moon's surface in the period of three hundred years or so that it has been under close observation. There is very considerable difficulty when it comes to comparing a small region of the moon's surface at widely separated times in ensuring that *all* the conditions are sufficiently unchanged to make the comparison valid. The moon's motion, including librations (wobblings), is so complex that sets of conditions of *precisely* the same aspect, with telescopes and equipment of exactly equal power, and under equal terrestrial conditions of air-steadiness and height above the horizon, are obviously almost impossible of certain attainment. So that claims to have detected small changes are well-nigh incapable of being completely established. Large-scale changes that could be seen irrespective of the fulfilment of these many conditions have certainly not occurred.

CAUSE OF THE CRATERS

One has only to look at a photograph of the moon's surface to be led to wonder how all the craters have been formed. There have been two main hypotheses put forward to account for them, which may be termed first, the volcanic theory, which ascribes them to causes internal to the moon, and second, the meteoritic theory, which ascribes them to the impact of meteorites coming from outside the moon.

According to the volcanic hypothesis, the lunar craters are simply extinct volcanoes, and the dark seas are lava beds at the low-lying regions of the lunar surface. The central peaks existing within some craters are considered to be the places at which the material was ejected long ago, and this material was thrown upwards and outwards radially, to pile up a considerable distance away and form the outer ring. But it is difficult to see why craters should be produced on the moon far greater in size than any known on the Earth; and there is the added difficulty that there is no close resemblance whatever between any volcanoes on the Earth and any lunar craters. Also, signs of lava flow on the moon are almost entirely lacking at places where, from the evident violence of the disturbance, they might be most expected. Even if the craters have been produced by volcanic eruptions, the process unlike that on Earth must have ceased, for there are no signs of any volcanic activity at the present time.

Although the volcanic hypothesis was at one time widely favoured, there does not seem much to recommend it today, and the alternative hypothesis of meteoritic impact seems to many to be both inescapable and completely satisfactory. It is known that the space between the planets is still sparsely occupied by small bodies (that is, small compared with the planets themselves) moving round the sun just as the planets themselves do, only in more elongated paths for the most part. As time goes on these bodies are necessarily being gradually swept up by the planets, and their associated moons, and it is the resulting collisions that are the basis of the meteoritic hypothesis.

Consider what would be involved in any such impact. The moon, with the Earth, is moving round the sun more or less in a circle at $18\frac{1}{2}$ miles a second, and one of these meteorites that could collide with it would be moving at an even greater speed in a path crossing that of the moon, so that, to take a definite and likely figure, we can imagine the impact speed to be of the order of thirty miles a second, but it could be somewhat greater or less than this according to the precise circumstances. Now the important point to appreciate is that an object moving as fast as this has, in virtue of its motion, an energy weight for weight compared with which that of any ordinary explosive like dynamite or T.N.T. is quite negligible. At thirty miles a second the energy of motion per ton is about two hundred and fifty times that of dynamite, while at forty miles a second it would be almost four hundred and fifty times as great. When such a fast moving object strikes the surface of the moon, the greater part of this energy of motion must be converted into local energy of heat motion as action necessarily takes place to stop the moving mass. And this means that the temperature of the immediately colliding materials is raised suddenly to several million degrees. This in turn means it is converted to gaseous form at tremendous pressure, while the density of the gas will be greater than the original density of the colliding materials. Only in this way can the incoming meteorite be stopped, and it will necessarily penetrate some distance into the surface, by a few times its own diameter, while this is taking place.

There must then result an explosion of a violence far and away surpassing anything yet contrived on Earth even by atom

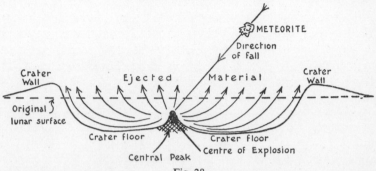

Fig. 28

Schematic drawing of meteoritic explosion producing a lunar crater. The explosion tries to throw out material in all directions, but immediately below the material can only be crushed, and a central peak is formed as shown.

The vertical scale is much exaggerated: the depths of actual craters are very shallow compared with their diameters. The direction of fall of the meteorite has practically no effect on the size and shape (circular) of the resulting crater

bombs, and this must blow out a vast quantity of material from the surrounding layers of the moon (Fig. 28). It is immediately obvious that the crater produced by such an explosion will be far larger in volume and extent than the incoming body itself. Also, for this very reason, it can matter little what direction the meteorite happens to fall in, vertically or obliquely, the resulting crater will always be more or less circular, because the explosion occurs outwards from the tremendously heated buried material, and must therefore be practically independent of the path by which the meteorite happened to arrive there. The depth of penetration before explosion occurred would obviously be somewhat less for impacts that were in a direction away from the vertical, but this would not affect the tendency for the resulting crater to be circular round the place to which the meteorite penetrated.

Accordingly the meteoritic hypothesis is able to account for the craters both as to their forms and their sizes. The range of these depends on the size of the meteorite and the speed at which it happens to be moving. The process of sweeping up stray meteorites has been going on for some four thousand million years, and what we see on the moon's surface are the outward signs of its modest contribution to the general spring-cleaning of space. Also, it seems highly probable that these collisions would have been more frequent in the earlier stages of the solar system, and decreasing as time went on, but even if they happened always at much the same rate, one collision every twenty thousand years could produce two hundred thousand craters during the lifetime of the Earth and moon, supposing them to have much the same age. Sizeable new craters that we could see from the Earth are therefore not going to appear on the average now more often than about once every twenty thousand years, at the shortest estimate. So although a new crater could appear at any time, it is not surprising that no new crater has been formed during the mere three hundred years or so that the moon has been under systematic observation.

If, however, we accept that the craters are due to impacts of objects coming from outside the moon, it is obviously against the laws of chance that there should be large areas, the seas, almost devoid of them, or at least containing far fewer area for area than occur elsewhere. So the meteoritic theory must introduce some other effects to account for this feature. The answer is simple enough, for it is clear that the "seas" themselves, such as the very circular Mare Crisium (the Sea of Crises) visible near the north-west limb, are almost certainly only the remains of really large craters, and that their areas necessarily therefore form low-lying plains on the moon. There must be some effect tending to fill in these low-lying areas, and their beautifully smooth surfaces in many instances are strongly suggestive of this. In that event, these areas can have received just as many impacts, but the craters so formed must now be lying buried beneath a deep layer of material capable of forming a smooth surface. Many examples of craters just peeping out of the seas are available to support this view.

As to what form the material may be in, or have been in to

get there, there are two obvious possibilities. The first is that of lava, which could obviously flow into low lying areas, and the second is that of very fine dust, though in this case the mechanism of flow to form smooth floors is less obvious. Nevertheless, this second suggestion now seems the more plausible. There being no atmosphere, the lunar surface is exposed to direct sunlight, and the strong ultra-violet light and X-rays can destroy the surface layers of exposed rocks and reduce them to dust at the rate of a few ten-thousandths of an inch per year. But even this minute amount could during the age of the moon be sufficient to form a layer over it several miles deep.

It remains only to explain how such dust could be moved about to fill in the low-lying areas, and there are several possible causes all of which could contribute. First, the small dust particles may behave rather like a very shallow atmosphere on the moon, in which case those particles at the outer surface are all the time in a state of agitated motion to a very small but nevertheless finite extent in all directions. A thermal motion of this kind alone would gradually cause the dust to flow to such low-lying areas as were accessible without involving the scaling of too great heights. Thus it might not be possible for such dust to "flow" over a high crater wall, and this may account for the fact that the level of the smooth floor within certain craters is different from that of the lunar surface immediately outside. The laying down of dust within a crater will be a local affair. Second, light pressure itself is able to exert a force on small particles whose sizes are of the same order as the wave-length of the light; this might help to keep dust just slightly in motion to enable it to reach an equilibrium distribution on the surface. There may also be other external effects, such as the arrival of interstellar particles, right down to individual molecules and atoms, moving at high speeds, assisting to keep the surface layer of dust in a state of agitation and thereby enabling it to flow gradually. It is a matter for the future to decide for certain about the presence of dust and the effects operating on it, but if we are to weigh the matter from the circumstantial evidence available at present, it seems far more probable that the meteoritic hypothesis is correct than that the volcanic one is, and accordingly that some fluid effect such as would be provided by dust is needed to account for the filling in of the seas and the covering over of many of the craters. What can be discovered from the appearance of these smooth surface areas and their capacity for absorbing and emitting light and heat is certainly not inconsistent with the dust hypothesis.

WHY IS NOT THE EARTH COVERED WITH CRATERS?

If the meteoritic hypothesis is regarded as satisfactorily explaining the lunar craters, we are immediately led to ask why the much bigger Earth has not also been similarly showered with meteorites, and therefore similarly strewn and corrugated with even more craters than the moon? Obviously, there is no possibility whatever of supposing that the Earth can have escaped such celestial attentions while at the same time supposing the moon to have received hundreds of thousands of them.

Let us take the meteoritic question first. It is known that small meteorites, weighing only a few pounds or so, are subject to very great resistance by the Earth's atmosphere, which quickly slows them up at the price of their becoming strongly heated in a thin surface layer by the friction of the air rushing past them. Specimens have actually been seen to fall, and their speeds have been so low that they scarcely penetrate the ground at all and simply lie where they fall. They show a characteristic thin surface layer where the material has been melted corresponding to this heating.

Even the passage of a small meteorite of a few pounds weight through the Earth's atmosphere is accompanied by a tremendous noise as it literally blazes its supersonic trail, and all this is part of the mechanism whereby its energy of motion is being reduced. All the resistance effects will depend more or less on the area of the object and will therefore increase as the square of its linear size, but the penetration effects will depend on the mass and so will go up as the cube of its size. So with increasing size of meteorite, the Earth's atmosphere will become less and less able to offer any strong resistance, and for meteorites weighing one hundred tons or more the Earth's solid surface is as exposed to them as openly and unprotectedly as if there were no atmosphere at all, as is in fact the case for the moon whatever size the meteorite.

The number of meteorites actually seen to fall on the Earth has averaged about six a year for the first half of this century, but obviously the total number arriving over the whole surface must be much greater. The majority, at least ninety per cent, are stones in the form of crystalline rocks, while three per cent are irons, and others are mixtures of stone and iron. Sometimes just one piece falls, but more usually there are several. It is possible that break-up occurs in the atmosphere because of the enormous aerodynamic forces that the air-resistance would produce at the surface of an irregularly shaped fast-moving body. At the Pultusk fall in 1869 it was estimated that a hundred thousand small meteorites fell together. The largest recovered masses have been the iron Ahnighito meteorite found by the explorer, Peary, near Cape York in Greenland, which weighs over thirty-six tons, and another at Grootfontein in South Africa weighing rather more than fifty tons. It may perhaps be mentioned in passing that it is specially interesting that these cosmical visitors are found to be made of just the same elements already found and well-known on Earth; they do not contain any "unknown" or "different" elements, or anything of such metaphysical kind, and instead provide strong evidence of the great uniformity of Nature throughout the universe.

The conclusion cannot be avoided that area for area a similar number of meteorites have arrived at the Earth's surface as have fallen on that of the moon. But where then are their craters? The first part of the answer is simple: namely, the effect of weather. The erosion and wearing down of stone and rocks proceeds at a terrific pace compared with the periods of time that are involved here. A moderate-sized crater, a few miles in size, formed even as recently as a few million years ago would long since have been completely obliterated by erosion and silting. This readily explains why the Earth is not completely covered and pock-marked with craters like the surface of the moon is. But it can still be asked why there are not at least a few recent ones that have not had time to be weathered away. There is no difficulty here, however, because in fact there are, quite a few. About a dozen known craters of the order of a mile or so in size have now been recognised and accepted as of fairly recent meteoritic origin. Most of them are situated in remote places, and mainly in desert areas where erosion is likely to have been slower.

CRATER

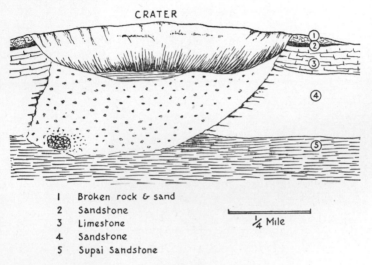

1   Broken rock & sand
2   Sandstone
3   Limestone
4   Sandstone
5   Supai Sandstone

¼ Mile

Fig. 29

Schematic drawing of cross-section of the Arizona crater. The remains of the meteorite are believed to be under one of the walls (suggesting oblique impact) as shown; it may actually consist of many shattered pieces

The best known is probably the great Arizona meteorite crater, which was described by Arrhenius, the great Swedish scientist, as "the most interesting spot on Earth." This is situated about thirty miles east of Flagstaff, and by a curious chance about midway between the celebrated Petrified Forest and the Painted Desert, while to the north is the Grand Canyon itself, so that within the one state of Arizona can be seen all these four strange natural phenomena. The meteorite crater is about two-thirds of a mile across in any direction and, although silted up somewhat, the floor is still about six hundred feet below the level of the surrounding plain. Its age is considered to be about forty- to fifty-thousand years.

The object that produced this crater has been estimated to have had a weight of about a million tons, the uncertainty depending on the incoming speed of course, which cannot be settled precisely. If it were a ball of iron it would have been about two hundred feet in diameter. But the crater itself would require about two thousand million tons of rock to fill it (Fig. 29). This brings out the point that the size of a crater is to be regarded as far larger than the object producing it: the hole is not due to the object merely drilling into the surface, but to the resulting explosion of a mass of gas at least equal to that of the meteorite suddenly raised to ten million degrees in temperature. The meteorite responsible for the Arizona crater is considered to have penetrated down a distance of about fifteen hundred feet (this would take about a hundredth of a second at a speed of thirty miles a second), though the explosion would occur before the meteorite was completely stopped, and what remains of it is believed now to be at about this depth below the base of the southern rim. Unfortunately, early attempts to mine for the object proceeded on the mistaken assumption that because the crater was nearly circular the meteorite must have fallen nearly vertically, and drilling straight down under from the middle failed to find anything.

The walls round the rim of this crater run up gently 150 feet or so above the surrounding plain and then on the inside descend steeply to the floor of the crater. The walls are a jumble of large boulders of sandstone and limestone. There are no signs of volcanic activity in the whole district. Thousands of iron meteorites have been found within the surrounding ten miles or so, while borings into the crater show that the rocks below have been crushed down to a depth of several hundred feet. The rocks also show evidence of great heating. All in all there is scarcely a shadow of doubt that the crater is meteoritic and not volcanic.

Another splendid example is the recently discovered Chubb crater in Ungava, just south of the Hudson Strait, in the remotest part of northern Quebec. The crater is nearly circular and about two miles in diameter, with the walls rising to more than five hundred feet above the level of the water now contained within the crater, whose depth itself is not yet known. The tops of the walls are about two hundred and fifty feet above the level of the surrounding territory outside the crater. Again, there are no signs of volcanic activity in the locality. The age of the crater is estimated to be somewhat in excess of three thousand years after a recent expedition organised to study the region.

Meteorites capable of forming either the Arizona or the Ungava crater would completely devastate a far larger region. A much smaller meteorite than either of them could wipe out a large city in an instant. A comparatively small meteorite, estimated at a few hundred tons, fell in a remote forest region of Siberia on 30 June 1908. The site was not explored till 1927 when it was found that an area at least twenty miles in radius had been devastated, and within this distance all trees, stripped of bark and branches, were lying with their tops directed away from the centre of the explosion. The blast wave was felt and intense noise is reported to have been heard four hundred miles away.

All the known recognised meteorite craters on the Earth, however, are only a few miles in diameter and therefore far smaller than the many large lunar ones, so finally we are led to ask whether there are any signs of really large craters on the Earth, comparable in size with the lunar seas. Now this is a question that has been little discussed, and yet is one that the meteoritic hypothesis certainly raises in a very pressing way. It must be said that there appears to be a widespread tendency to fight shy of any suggestion that the processes by which astronomical bodies form may still be going on, and while for the planets further serious growth is unlikely, there seems no valid reason to dismiss the idea that they may have formed to a large extent by the addition of material at their surfaces; that is, by the cumulative effect of this very same meteoritic bombardment. In face of this general prevailing attitude, it would be thought highly speculative and controversial to suggest that any of the larger surface features of the Earth, such as the distribution of the land and water areas, could possibly be of meteoritic origin, but I would ask the reader to take an atlas of the world and study it carefully with the general idea of lunar craters in mind. Consider for instance the region of the Gulf of Mexico and the Caribbean Sea, the enclosed seas of Europe, and a host of other areas, and last but not least the great areas of the oceanic deeps themselves.

A VISIT TO THE MOON

Having now discovered what effects are most likely to be responsible for the moon's surface features, let us consider what kinds of conditions might await the first visitor to the moon, if ever that should become possible. We will pass over all the immense difficulties of getting there and suppose we are at liberty to choose a landing site. We cannot of course be sure of the conditions, but we must reckon on the invitingly smooth level surfaces being deep seas of fine dust into which we would sink and be submerged unless we had special equipment available and ready to overcome this. Otherwise our only hope of getting about would be to stick to the mountainous rims of the craters. If the sun were up, the ground under our feet would be as hot as boiling water, and the sun's light, with its ultra-violet rays completely unscreened, would very soon prove blinding and lethal, unless we had special protection from it. There would be not an atom of air to breathe, and not a drop of water in any shape or form. If we decided to land round on the dark side, it would be so cold as to make the worst Siberian winter seem like a heat-wave. The only possible source of joy, apart from the mere novelty of being on the moon, might be to look up at the heavens where we would see a large brilliant object in the sky silently looking down on us; and it would be our own Earth to which we could never return.

So adverse to life are the conditions on the moon, we may therefore conclude that it is scarcely worthwhile at the present time to think other than in terms of sending some projectile to our satellite containing only scientific equipment but no passengers. When the time comes near even for this limited project to be practicable, the main problems will be to decide exactly what should be sent in the projectile with a view to determining the lunar conditions. However great the circumstantial evidence in favour of the meteoritic hypothesis, only by direct means will the matter be finally and conclusively settled.

REFERENCES

Map of the Moon (29 inches by 19½ inches), Elger and Wilkins,
G. Philip, London.

The Moon, W. H. Pickering, New York, 1903.

The Face of the Moon, R. B. Baldwin, Chicago, 1949.

Meteorites, O. C. Farrington, Chicago, 1915.

The Lunar Surface, T. Gold, Monthly Notices of the Royal
Astronomical Society, 1955.

1. The Earth from a rocket at a height of about 150 miles over Arizona. To the left is the Gulf of California, and beyond that the Pacific Ocean. The far horizon, showing the Earth's curvature, is over a thousand miles away.

2. The Midnight Sun. The sun's path in the sky as seen in late July over Smith Sound, near Etah, Greenland, about 12° from the North pole. Eight exposures at 20-minute intervals, four on each side of midnight.

3. The Moon at First Quarter: 7 days old. Less of the area is covered by dark seas and this half of the moon is brighter than the other half. Compare the position and apparent shape of the dark sea on the left (Mare Crisium 250 miles diameter) with Plate 4, the change is due to libration in longitude. (South at the top.)

4. The Full Moon: 14 days old. An arid ball of rock 2160 miles in diameter. At this aspect the "seas" look darkest, and the streaks radiating from Tycho in the south (at top in picture) and other craters show most clearly.

5. The Moon at Third Quarter: 22 days old. Note the crater Plato (60 miles across) with its smooth floor, on the north edge of the great Mare Imbrium (bottom of picture); Copernicus is at its southern edge near the centre of the picture. The rays from Tycho are now almost invisible. Compare the position of Plato in Plate 4, the change is due

6. Part of the north-east quadrant of the moon at third quarter, taken with the 100 inch telescope. To the right and south of the smooth-floored Plato are the Alps. Due south of Plato, and also with a smooth floor, is the crater Archimedes. Near the bottom left is Copernicus, with radiating streaks and rays, and to the right of it is Eratosthenes, both showing central peaks. Notice the innumerable small craters in the seas, though far fewer than elsewhere. (In this picture north is at the top.)

7. The huge crater Clavius, taken with the 200 inch telescope. About 140 miles across. It appears elliptical because it is far south (see Plate 4) and we are not looking straight down on it. Notice how its walls are eroded and broken into by other smaller craters, and the large number of small ones within its otherwise fairly smooth floor. (North at the top.)

8. The Arizona Meteorite Crater. Nearly a mile across and 700 feet deep. Notice the raised rim sloping gently down outside to the surrounding desert plain. The sun is low on the left leaving half the crater in shadow.

9. A group of volcanic craters in Java. Their conical forms bear little resemblance to lunar craters or to terrestrial meteorite craters. **10** (*inset*). The Ungava meteorite crater, recently discovered in remote northern Quebec. Aerial photograph from 20,000 feet. It is about 2 miles in diameter with walls rising 500 feet above the level of the lake partially filling it.

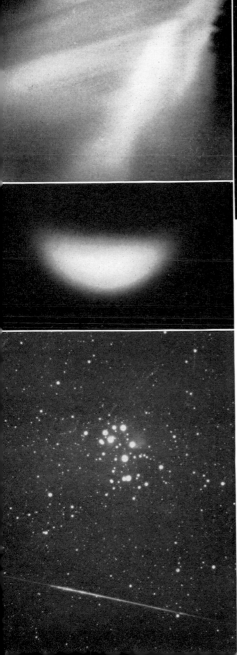

11. A meteor streaks past the Pleiades. The meteor is a tiny dust particle from interplanetary space entering our atmosphere at high speed and seen 50 or 60 miles up. The stars of the cluster are about 350 light-years away—about 30 million million times as distant as the meteor.

12. Mercury as seen near its furthest angular distance from the sun in June 1934. The phase shows clearly, but the markings on the surface of the planet can be detected only on the original negative.

13. An auroral curtain photographed at Professor Störmer's auroral station at Askim, Norway, January 1938. The nearly vertical rays were red in colour and the lower arc to the left green.

14. The Ahnighito Meteorite: 36½ tons of nickel-iron. Found by Peary in 1895 near Cape York, Greenland. The largest museum specimen; on view at the Hayden Planetarium, New York City.

15. The planet Venus at five different phases, from full when furthest from the Earth to crescent when nearest. The change in apparent size results from the planet's motion round the sun in a path lying entirely inside that of the Earth.

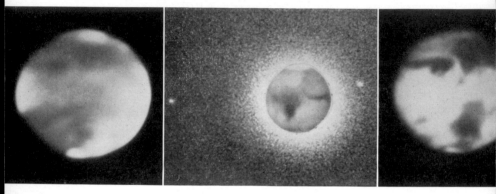

16. Mars photographed in blue light (200 inch telescope). This does not penetrate the atmosphere well, and surface markings are scarcely visible, though the north polar cap can be seen. 17 (centre). Mars and its tiny satellites, 17 August 1924. Phobos is to the right of the planet, and Deimos to the left considerably fainter. The image of the planet itself has been printed separately with a shorter exposure. 18. Mars photographed in red light (200 inch telescope). This penetrates the atmosphere and reveals the dark surface markings. (North on the planet is at the bottom of the picture.)

19. Jupiter photographed in blue light (200 inch telescope), showing the great red spot and equatorial belts of the atmosphere. Note the oblate form due to rapid rotation. The largest satellite Ganymede is visible just above to the right of the planet and its shadow on the disc above the great red spot.

20. Saturn and its ring system. The outermost ring (nearly 100,000 miles in radius) appears fainter because it has fewer particles, and the dark Cassini division probably almost none. Notice the atmospheric belts. The shadow of the planet on the ring can be seen next to top right of the disc, and the planet can be seen *through* the ring at the lowest part.

21 (*left*). Uranus and its five satellites. The planet is much over-exposed to get the tiny fifth satellite Miranda, discovered in 1948 (to be seen at about 2 o'clock relative to the planet). The other bright satellites are Ariel, Umbriel, Titania, and Oberon, in order of increasing distance. **22** (*right*). Neptune and its second satellite Nereid, discovered in 1949, indicated by arrow at top right. The planet has been much over-exposed to obtain the very faint satellite. (Each of the many faint dots is a separate background star.) **23** (*inset*). Neptune and its larger satellite Triton.

24 and **25**. The outermost planet Pluto, showing its motion in 3 days relative to the fixed background stars, March 2 (*left*) to March 5 (*right*), 1930. It is this motion that distinguishes it as a planet,

26. The apparition of Halley's comet in 1066 as depicted on the famous Bayeux tapestry. "These men are marvelling at the star!"

27. Halley's comet in 1910 (4 May), showing the tail streaming away from. t. The head is over-exposed in order to bring out the tail. (The little streaks are background stars that trail on the plate as the camera follows the slight orbital motion of the comet.) Notice how stars are visible through the tail.

The sun during a partial eclipse: no trace of the corona is visible. **29.** The "diamond-ring" effect. Total
pse has just ended, and as the photosphere reappears it seems far larger than it really is because of its
ense light. The inner corona can still be seen. **30.** Total eclipse of 1919 May 29. Showing the lower
t of the corona and a gigantic solar prominence. **31.** Total eclipse of 1954 June 30. Showing the
atorial extensions of the corona, and the well-defined polar brushes suggestive of lines of force of a
gnet. **32.** Total eclipse of 1952 February 25. Showing the form that the corona assumes at a time
r sunspot minimum; equatorial streamers are then always strong. **33.** Total eclipse of 1929 May 9.
wing the form of the corona at a time near sunspot maximum. The corona is then always more or
symmetrical. (A great prominence is visible on the left limb.)

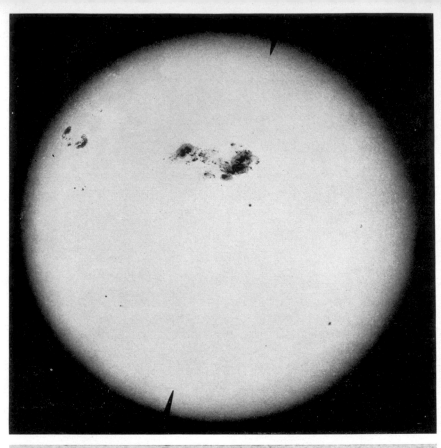

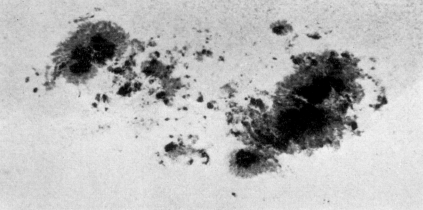

34. The spotted sun. The gigantic spot group of 1947 April 7, nearly 200,000 miles across. (The pointers show the positions of the poles of the sun, north at the bottom.) The sun looks darker nearer its edge, as the picture shows, because the light is there coming out sideways through a greater depth of atmosphere.

The lower picture shows the spot group magnified up fourfold, and brings out the different degrees of darkness of the umbra and the penumbra. This picture also reveals the granulated appearance of the turbulent photosphere.

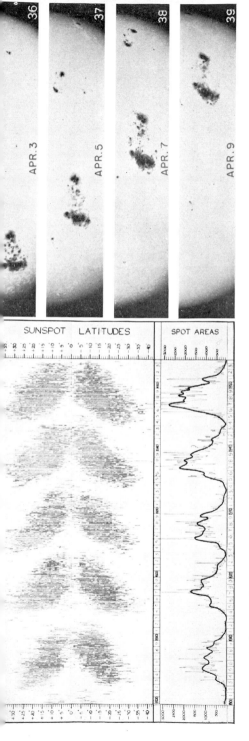

36-39. The position of a spot group at intervals two days apart. The rotation of the sun appears to carry a spot across the disc. (1947.)

35. The distribution of sunspots with latitude on the sun's surface, showing how as the cycle proceeds the region where spots form drifts towards the equator. Below this is the sunspot curve from 1900 showing the fraction of the area of the sun (in millionths) covered each day by spots.

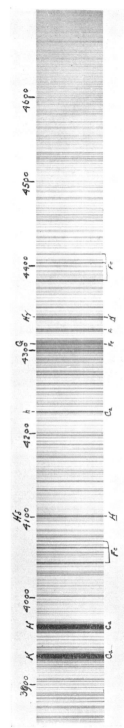

40. A part of the solar spectrum towards the violet end. The numbers give wavelengths. Below are the symbols for the elements producing the lines. The dark H and K lines of calcium are prominent near the extreme left.

41. The Cambridge radio-telescope. The parabolic supports carry wires running the length of the system, and these focus the waves at the central crosses, from which they are led into the receivers.

42. The "Crab" nebula in Taurus. Taken in red light with the 200 inch telescope. This cloud within our galaxy is expanding at nearly 1000 miles a second and is now about 30 million million miles across. It is believed to be a product of the supernova explosion there seen in A.D. 1054. This cloud is a powerful transmitter of radio-noise.

43. The "Horse's Head" nebula in Orion. In red light (200 inch). One of the many dark irregularly shaped dust clouds in our galaxy. This dark nebula is several million million miles across.

44 (*left*). Region of the Southern Cross: a portion of the Milky Way. The over-exposed stars are two of the visible stars of the Southern Cross, and the large dark region a dust cloud, popularly known as "the Coalsack." Each tiny bright speck is a brilliant star. **45** (*right*). The Globular Cluster in Hercules (200 inch). Each dot is a brilliant star. About 100,000 stars go to make up one of these clusters.

46. The spiral nebula N.G.C. 4594 in Virgo. This galaxy is about 30 million light-years away. The dark band is obscuration by dust clouds within the system. Some of the faint dots immediately above and below it are associated globular clusters.

47 (*left*). The barred spiral N.G.C. 7741 in the constellation of Pegasus. This type of spiral is characterised by the curious bright central bar. The whole system consists of stars, gas and dust clouds. 48 (*right*). The spiral nebula M 51 in Canes Venatici. This was the first galaxy observed to have spiral structure. The smaller object below it is probably a companion nebula.

49. The famous Andromeda nebula, M 31. This spiral galaxy is a companion to our own and believed to be practically a twin of it as regards size and general shape. About 1,500,000 light-years away. The only external galaxy perceptible to the unaided eye, and easily the most distant object so visible.

50. The spiral nebula M 81 in the constellation of Ursa Major. One of the most perfect examples. About 5,000,000 light-years away from us.

N.G.C. 4565. The edge-on spiral in Coma Berenices (200 inch telescope). All these objects consist of stars, gas, and dust clouds.

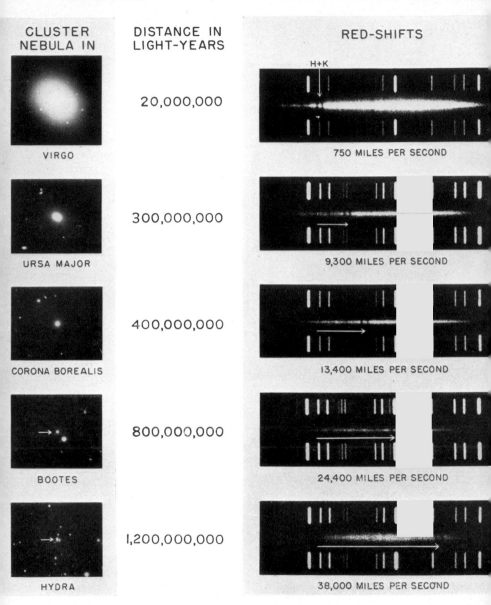

CLUSTER NEBULA IN	DISTANCE IN LIGHT-YEARS	RED-SHIFTS
VIRGO	20,000,000	H+K 750 MILES PER SECOND
URSA MAJOR	300,000,000	9,300 MILES PER SECOND
CORONA BOREALIS	400,000,000	13,400 MILES PER SECOND
BOOTES	800,000,000	24,400 MILES PER SECOND
HYDRA	1,200,000,000	38,000 MILES PER SECOND

52. The nebulae decrease in apparent size with distance almost in proportion, because they are of roughly equal actual dimensions. (The clear vertical lines above and below each spectrum on the right are those of a comparison spectrum put on for measurement.) The pair of dark H and K lines of calcium are visible in each spectrum, and their displacement from their standard position (shown by arrows) measures the amount of the so-called "red-shift."

III

THE PLANETS AND COMETS

The Earth a planet—Gravitation—Planetary orbits—Mercury—Theory of Relativity—Venus —Mars—Possibility of life on Mars—Satellites— Jupiter—Surface appearance—Satellites of Jupiter—Saturn—Ring system and Satellites— Uranus and Neptune—Discovery of Neptune— Satellites—Temperature and Atmosphere of outer planets—Pluto—Former satellite of Neptune?— Motions of planets—Asteroids—Relation to meteorites—Comets—Number and paths— Long-period comets—Short-period comets— Halley's comet—Sizes and masses—Tails— Nature of comets—Dust particles—Meteor streams—Recurrence of meteor showers—Table of planetary data.

THE FORCE OF GRAVITATION

When we look up at the sky on a clear night we see in all directions countless stars. Their positions seem never to change except for the general steady rotation of them all round the pole-star, as though they were attached to a huge rotating dome, in a motion that simply reflects the Earth's daily rotation. But often to be seen amongst these fixed stars are a few conspicuous bright objects, looking rather like stars, but slowly moving in the sky. These are the planets; and the first great step of modern science was the recognition that the Earth itself must be counted one of these. That is, our own seemingly solid Earth is moving swiftly through space round the sun, but with such perfect steadiness that we are entirely unconscious of the motion.

Just as the moon moves round the Earth, so the Earth and planets move round the sun, and there must therefore be some force operating to keep these bodies moving in the way they do. Similarly there must be an attraction on the moon, otherwise it would fly off at a tangent. The necessary attraction is the force of gravitation, the existence of which was first clearly perceived by Newton. The same force that holds everybody and everything down on the surface of the Earth is keeping the moon circling round it, and also keeping the Earth circling round the sun. If this force of gravitation were to cease, and we decided nevertheless to keep our moon by attaching it to the Earth by a steel cable, it would have to be at least five hundred miles thick to stand the strain. This gives some idea of the force that gravitation is able to exert across empty space to hold the moon to the Earth. But when it comes to the force required to hold the Earth to the sun, the cable would have to be more than five thousand miles thick to stand the strain. The force required is about five million million million tons, so it would obviously need a pretty stout cable if it were not to snap under such a load.

These forces are in fact supplied by gravitation, as aforesaid, and the sun presides in the middle of the solar system simply because it has practically all the gravitational power, that is, because of its great mass. The sun weighs about seven hundred

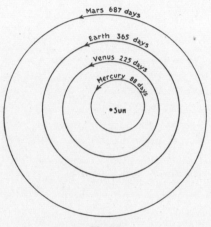

Fig. 30

The paths of the four inner planets. The orbits of Venus and the Earth are almost circular, but that of Mercury and to a less extent that of Mars are distinctly elliptical with the sun at one focus. The paths lie nearly in the same plane. (The inclinations of the planes of the paths to that of the Earth are Mercury 7°, Venus 3°24′, and Mars 1°51′)

times as much as all the planets put together, and the planets move round the sun in more or less circular paths—they are actually slightly elliptical in varying degrees. They all travel round in the same general direction and roughly in the same plane, so that the solar system is a flat open structure, as far as the planets are concerned. Fig. 30 shows the arrangement of the paths round the sun of the four innermost planets, Mercury, Venus, the Earth, and Mars, that make up the so-called terrestrial group. Fig. 31 shows the orbits of the four great outer planets, Jupiter, Saturn, Uranus, and Neptune, together with that of the far smaller planet Pluto. Once again, there is this difficulty of scale that makes it awkward to represent even the orbits, on one and the same diagram, for all the planets; Mercury is only about two-fifths the Earth's distance from the

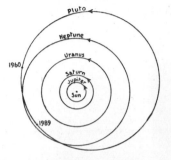

Fig. 31

The paths of the four great outer planets, Jupiter, Saturn, Uranus, and Neptune; and also that of the tiny Pluto. Neptune moves at 30 times the Earth's distance from the sun. The path of Pluto is inclined at about 17° to the general plane in which the other planets move, and it comes *inside* that of Neptune, as shown

sun, whereas Pluto averages nearly forty times this distance, giving a ratio of just about one hundred between the greatest and least planetary distances.

MERCURY

If we start at the sun and imagine ourselves moving outwards, the first of the planets we would come to would be the tiny Mercury. It is just over three thousand miles in diameter, half as great again as the moon, and always turns the same face to the sun, just as the moon always turns the same face to the Earth. The rotation period of Mercury on its axis is therefore the same as its orbital period of motion round the sun, which is eighty-eight days.

Generally the planet is so near the sun that it can be observed only by day, at morning or evening according to circumstances. Like all planets, its light is entirely due to reflected sunlight, and it shows phases as it goes round the sun, in much the same way as does the moon. When best visible it appears nearly as luminous as Sirius though in a strong twilight sky. Only under the most favourable atmospheric conditions can any surface details be seen on it even with powerful telescopes, and reliable observers describe these as resembling in a general way those seen on the moon with the unaided eye. As in the case of the moon, this planet is too small to hold any atmosphere, especially in view of the high temperature that its proximity to the sun will ensure. The sunlit side is maintained at a temperature of over 300° C., hot enough to melt lead, while the side in permanent darkness must be intensely cold.

The path round the sun is inclined at about seven degrees to

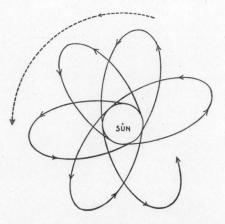

Fig. 32

The theory of relativity slightly modifies the law of gravitation near the sun, and as a result Mercury does not move in a fixed ellipse but in a slowly rotating one. The ellipse turns right round once in about 3 million years. The phenomenon itself was detected long before the advent of the relativity theory and is termed "the advance of the perihelion of Mercury"

the plane in which the Earth moves round the sun, but only rarely does the little planet appear to pass directly across the disc of the sun as seen from the Earth. Such an occurrence is called a *transit* of Mercury, and the planet then appears as a small black dot against the brilliant face of the sun.

Apart from the tiny Pluto which we shall come to last of all, Mercury has the most eccentric of all the planetary orbits, and it is this feature (together with its closeness to the sun) that enabled it to give the first decisive test of the theory of relativity.

If Mercury were affected only by simple gravitation of the sun, the orbit would be an ellipse and the direction of the axis of this orbit would remain fixed. But according to small corrections to the law of gravitation discovered by Einstein, the orbit ought to rotate in its own plane, and the elongated form of the path would make this easier to detect (Fig. 32). This was known to occur and it had long been one of the mysteries of astronomy why the orbit did in fact rotate. The clearing up of this profound difficulty was one of Einstein's great triumphs.

VENUS

Next we come to the beautiful planet Venus, which in some ways is very similar to the Earth. The sun and moon apart, Venus is the brightest object in the heavens. It also is seen only in mornings and evenings, but on occasions is wonderfully well situated for observation. It goes through all the phases, but it is not quite possible to discern them with the unaided eye. Venus is permanently shrouded with brilliant white clouds that strongly reflect the sun's light and prevent us seeing what its solid surface may be like. That Venus possesses an atmosphere is plainly evident at and near inferior conjunction when the planet is more or less directly between the sun and Earth. It then appears in thin crescent form, and the horns of the crescent are seen to extend beyond the mere half-circle, showing that more than half the planet is illuminated by the sun. In other words that there is an atmospheric twilight effect.

Even the length of the day on Venus is difficult to determine, because the planet rotates so very slowly, and all that is certain is that it is much longer than our own day. It may even equal the length of the year for Venus, that is, the time the planet takes to go round the sun, which is 225 days. Something has evidently happened to slow the rotation of Venus up much more than has happened even to the Earth. The reason is not known, but it is inviting to think that Mercury may have once been a large moon of Venus and was highly effective in slowing the rotation of the planet up by tidal action, as the moon is still doing to the Earth. The accompanying gradual increase in the distance of the satellite would also result in Mercury eventually escaping from Venus and becoming an independent body moving round the sun, and the present non-circularity of its path may even be a surviving remnant of this.

Although Venus is very similar in weight and size to the Earth, it must have undergone a very different evolution, judging by such parts of its atmosphere as can be investigated. The quality of the light it reflects shows no evidence of nitrogen, oxygen, or water vapour, though there is an abundance of carbon dioxide. It therefore seems improbable that Earthly creatures or plant life would stand much chance of surviving long on Venus.

MARS

Passing now beyond the Earth's orbit, we come to the famous planet Mars. Its diameter is a little over four thousand miles and it has about a tenth the weight of the Earth. Mars has a clear atmosphere that allows us to see down to the pinkish solid surface, suggestive of desert sands, which gives the planet its characteristic ruddy-orange colour. It is possible to detect the effects of twilight, and at times of fog, clouds, and haze on Mars. Numerous well-defined dark markings can be seen on the surface that change through the Martian year, which is 687 of our days in length.

Under the best conditions of clear-seeing these dark areas, according to some observers, sometimes seem to be joined by even more elusive darkish lines. It is these that are termed the "canals," and have been the source of so much speculation. But please do not get the impression that they are actual canals, or that the fine lines even necessarily exist. Towards the end of the last century some astronomers went so far as to believe that they were evidence of vast irrigation systems on the planet, and accordingly proof of the existence of conscious thinking beings who had constructed them. But the consensus of opinion today is that even the reality of the fine dark lines is more than doubtful, and much of the detail allegedly "seen" by these astronomers is now considered to have been mainly of the nature of optical illusion, due to complex personal equation and always likely to enter near the limit of seeing. No photograph has ever shown any definite evidence of them.

Nevertheless Mars certainly has an atmosphere that could possibly support life. Its presence is most clearly proved by the polar ice-caps which alternate from one pole to the other with the Martian seasons, showing that water-vapour is transported through the atmosphere just as it is on Earth. The caps shrink almost to nothing in one hemisphere during summer there and at the same time increase in area at the other pole where it is winter. They are probably thin layers of snow or frost: thin because they disappear so quickly. The atmosphere can also be detected otherwise from the imprint it puts upon the sunlight we receive reflected from the surface of the planet. It shows definite traces of both oxygen and water-vapour—elements indispensable to life—and so, quite apart from the highly controversial issue of the alleged "canals," the presence of these gases has kept open the great question "Is there life on Mars ?" But I think the large majority of astronomers if they were forced today to answer this question would say, that of animal or human life as we know it here on Earth, then certainly there can be none, though there might just conceivably have been in the past when oxygen and water-vapour may have been more abundant. Grim austerity conditions at best prevail on the planet, but plant life of very primitive forms might still exist, such as the moss lichens of the kinds one sees here on Earth on exposed rocks and ancient garden walls. However, it must be admitted that no one can be absolutely certain on this question, because it is not known what diverse forms life might take on to adjust itself to changing conditions if it once existed.

Several messages have been sent to Mars, or at any rate attempted, by wireless broadcasts. Two telegrams were despatched by the G.P.O. on behalf of members of the public about twenty-five years ago, and another quite recently by Bromley Abbott (of the *Sunday Dispatch*), as a result of my reference to the earlier ones on Television. But these hardly constitute a fair test because of the improbability of even a well-organised radio-system (on Mars) picking up so occasional a message from an unexpected direction (the Earth), and, moreover, as far as one is aware no adequate arrangements were made to receive any return signals.

A curious feature of Mars is that it possesses two tiny moons —named Phobos and Deimos—each only a few miles in diameter and visible only with the largest telescopes. The nearer one, Phobos, completes its circuit of the planet in only seven hours, whereas the planet itself rotates once in about twenty-four and a half hours. As a result, for an observer on Mars, this satellite rises in the west and sets in the east, completing this strange backward motion in about eleven hours. But the other one, Deimos, behaves normally and rises in the east and sets in the west, as a good well-conducted satellite should. They seem very likely to be captured asteroids rather than genuine moons.

JUPITER

Continuing on outwards from the sun, the next major planet we come to is the mighty Jupiter, who takes nearly twelve years to circle the sun. He easily outweighs all the rest of the planets put together, being some 318 times as massive as the Earth. This planet is also the largest, being nearly 90,000 miles in diameter. But despite his great mass, Jupiter is much less dense than the Earth (only about a quarter as dense in fact) mainly because it has an enormously deep atmosphere, composed of gases such as methane and ammonia, but only the very outermost layers of these can of course be seen.

The planet bulges out at the equator and is correspondingly flattened towards the poles, much more than is the Earth. This happens because the planet rotates so very fast, once in about ten hours, and the speed at the equator is about 27,000 miles an hour, far greater than the equatorial speed on Earth. The force of gravity on Jupiter is greater too, nearly three times as much, but not proportionately so, and the balance between them results in this greater bulginess than in the case of the Earth.

The planet also shows the streaked markings of the great equatorial currents that flow round in the atmosphere, and there is also conspicuous the mysterious "great red spot." It is sometimes seen as brick-red in colour, covering an oval region about 30,000 miles by 7,000 miles in extent, but the degree of redness changes and dims as though it were sometimes covered with haze. It has been conjectured that it may be due to volcanic action from far below, but little is known of what really goes on in Jupiter's atmosphere. This is not very surprising, since the planet when at its nearest is four hundred million miles away, and even then we can see only the outermost fringe of its atmosphere. Besides, those who know most about our own atmosphere, which we actually live in and can study at first hand, are only too conscious of how little is known about *it*. The weather is one of its minor complexities, and everyone knows how difficult that is to predict and understand.

Quite recently radio-waves have been detected coming from Jupiter, and are attributed to violent electrical effects in its atmosphere, so possibly there are terrific Jovian thunderstorms occurring on the planet, though in the absence of water-vapour these would be likely to be very different from our terrestrial thunderstorms.

Jupiter is very richly endowed with moons. There are four large ones, called the Galilean satellites, after Galileo their discoverer, each of which is very similar in size and weight to our own moon. This may be pure coincidence or it may afford an important clue to their origin. All four can easily be seen with ordinary field glasses, and under perfect conditions of seeing at high altitude stations have on occasion been seen with the unaided eye. These particular satellites have played a very important part in the history of science. When Galileo first saw them revolving round the planet he realised at once that it was the final nail in the coffin of the idea that the Earth must be the centre of the universe. His opponents, to give them due credit, must also have realised this equally clearly, because they refused all invitations to look through the telescope! The satellites were also made use of by Roemer in 1675 to establish that light travels with a finite speed and is not propagated instantaneously from place to place as had been thought.

Besides the difficult question of their origin, there are still unsolved problems connected with these four moons: why for instance does the second one take almost exactly twice as long as the first to circle the planet, and why does the third take almost exactly twice as long as the second, while the motion of the fourth one bears no such relationship to that of the third? The working out of their motions although an intricate problem has been solved, but the explanation of these peculiarities and how they have come about is not even in sight. It may not be difficult in the end, but it wants an idea, and no one seems to have had the right idea yet.

Now besides these four bright satellites, Jupiter has eight tiny faint ones, some of which can only be detected with the most powerful telescopes. The largest of these are only about one hundred miles in diameter and the smallest less than about twenty miles. Whereas the large inner ones take only a matter of days to go round the planet, some of these smaller ones move at greater distances and take about one or two years, and the four outermost of them even have the temerity to go round backwards. They are almost certainly comparatively recent captures of asteroids (minor planets) made by Jupiter, and shed little light on the question of the origin of the other main ones, which seem equally certainly to have originated at the same time as Jupiter itself.

SATURN

We come next to Saturn, nearly twice as far out from the sun as Jupiter, and taking $29\frac{1}{2}$ years to go round the central sun. Of all the planets this one provides the greatest surprise with its incredible ring system, which has no known counterpart anywhere else in the universe. It has been described as the most beautiful object in the whole of inanimate Nature. It was first vaguely seen by Galileo, but his not very powerful telescope showed it only as two curious appendages on each side of the planet, and he could make nothing of them.

It happens to be possible to go a very long way towards discovering what the rings are by purely theoretical considerations based on the law of gravitation. First, the rings cannot possibly be made of gas or liquid; this can be proved mathematically. It can also be proved that they cannot be a solid continuous ring, like a gigantic teething-ring, for if the system were so constituted, the ring would be unstable and on the slightest disturbance would dash itself against the planet and be destroyed. One may wonder then if it is neither solid, liquid, nor gas, what is left for it to be? The answer is that it consists of myriads of tiny separate solid particles, each moving round the planet independently and reflecting sunlight like a tiny moon—that is how the ring is made visible—the whole vast assembly going to make up the ring.

There are numerous other proofs of this. Parts of the ring are transparent, and the stars passing behind when in line with some parts are reduced in brightness, while when behind other parts, such as the Cassini division, they shine with their full brightness. Again, the inner edge of the ring moves faster round the planet than does the outer edge, whereas if it were a solid rotating ring the reverse would obviously hold. Moreover, the speeds at both edges are precisely what a freely moving satellite of Saturn at these distances should have. The main division in the ring, and the different intensities of brightness that it shows at different parts, are due to a thinning out of the particles at those places, there being fewer area for area than at parts where it appears brighter.

Every fifteen years the motion of the planet takes it to a point where the Earth is in the plane defined by the ring, so that the ring-system is then seen exactly edge on. At these times the ring completely disappears from view for several days even in the most powerful telescopes, thereby proving that the ring must be extremely thin—at most a few miles thick, as an upper limit—but in all probability it is very much thinner than this, possibly only one particle thick in depth, which might mean only a minute fraction of an inch thick.

How the ring came to be formed is not by any means a settled question, but the obvious explanation that it is a satellite that came too near the planet to withstand its strong tidal forces to remain stable, and therefore broke up, has been current and widely accepted for upwards of a century. On the other hand, although the idea has been little discussed, the ring is far more likely to represent a captured comet, because comets are known to consist already of enormous swarms of small particles, whereas it is doubtful if the break-up of a large body like a satellite would produce only small particles. The ring, by the way, has an overall diameter of nearly 200,000 miles and is about 40,000 miles across from inner edge to outer edge, and there is a clear space of nearly 8,000 miles between it and the outermost part of the planet.

The planet itself is not dissimilar to Jupiter, but it is only about one-third as massive, only half as dense, and a little smaller. Saturn is also much flattened towards the poles and bulged out at the equator, but even more so than is Jupiter, not only because of its rapid rotation in $10\frac{1}{2}$ hours but because of its lower density.

Saturn is also richly supplied with satellites, nine being known, ranging in size from about 3,500 miles in diameter in the case of the largest, Titan, to about 200 miles in the case of the tiny Phoebe, which incidentally goes round backwards. It is Titan, we may note, that is believed to be responsible for the main division in the ring, as a result of the disturbing influence that its mass produces on the paths of the particles at that distance, but there must be some secondary effect tending to widen the gap, such as possibly collisions between the particles themselves. Many questions of this sort are still far from having been satisfactorily settled.

URANUS AND NEPTUNE

All these five planets from Mercury to Saturn are at times extremely bright objects easily visible to the naked eye and were well-known to the ancients. They were never in any sense "discovered," any more than the moon can have been. But there are three more planets further out still from the sun that have actually been discovered within the past two-hundred years. First among these is Uranus, with period eighty-four years, almost exactly twice as far from the sun as Saturn. Then next we come to Neptune, about half as far away again, and taking 165 years to circle the sun. The first of these two was discovered more or less accidentally by Herschel in 1781, and was for a time thought to be a faint comet.

Neptune was found in 1846, but in this case as a result of theoretical calculations. Detailed instructions where to look for it were sent to the Berlin observatory by the famous French astronomer Leverrier, who had spent many years deciding where a hypothetical planet should move that could change the motion of Uranus by the small amounts that it had been found to be out of place from its expected and calculated path since its own discovery more than half a century earlier. This second discovery was hailed then and long afterwards as the greatest triumph of the human intellect to date—perhaps a little over-enthusiastically one thinks today. But it was destined to precipitate a bitter international controversy, for the reason that a young and then unknown Cambridge mathematician, John Couch Adams, had already successfully tackled the same problem quite independently, having actually communicated the position of the theoretical planet, and suggested a search, to the reigning Astronomer Royal, Sir George Airy, many months before. For various reasons nothing effective was done about it and the indisputable priority for this country was lost. But fortunately there were some Englishmen courageous enough to speak up for Adams—he himself was far too modest to have done so, though on the other side of the Channel this was interpreted in some quarters as the crudest attempt to take away the credit from France. Not all the subsequent discussion took place in the politest terms, but the people concerned have long since departed this life, and both Leverrier and Adams today share the credit, now everywhere accepted as men thoroughly capable of carrying out the necessary investigation, though it is still uncertain to exactly what extent both may have been facilitated by good fortune resulting from the particular configuration of the planets at the time and enabling their methods to work.

Curiously enough the two planets, Uranus and Neptune, are very similar. Each is about 30,000 miles in diameter, and about fifteen or sixteen times the Earth's mass. But Uranus rotates in only $10\frac{1}{2}$ hours, whereas Neptune takes nearly 16. Uranus has four main satellites, Ariel, Umbriel, Titania, and Oberon, but a fifth closer and much smaller one, named Miranda, has very recently been discovered. Neptune for a long time was thought to have but one satellite, Triton, which, though moving quite close to the planet like most normal satellites, strangely enough goes round backwards in its path, that is in the opposite direction to the rotation of the planet. A recent discovery however has also added a small faint satellite, now called Nereid, to the Neptune system.

Going back to Uranus, its rotation presents one of the most puzzling features in the whole solar system. Instead of the axis of rotation, as in the case of all the other planets, being fairly upright to the general plane in which all the planets move round the sun, it is lying over on its side, being tipped a little more than half way over so that on the whole the planet must be regarded as rotating backwards. This must make for the most curious conditions on Uranus. During the eighty-four of our years that it takes to go round the sun, at one stage the sun must be more or less permanently overhead at the one pole with the other hemisphere almost all in darkness, while forty-two years later the situation will be completely reversed and the sun will be practically overhead at the other pole. The satellites move in the plane of the equator of the planet defined by this axis of rotation, and so move in paths almost perpendicular to the plane in which Uranus moves round the sun.

All four of these great outer planets are at extremely low temperatures, at least –150 degrees centigrade, unimaginably colder than the severest polar conditions on Earth. Moreover, their deep atmospheres are composed mainly of poisonous gases, methane and ammonia, quite inimical to all forms of animal life, and contain no signs of oxygen or water-vapour. So they are about as unpromising abodes for any form of life as can be imagined, and we can be quite certain that they are utterly devoid of any form of life whatever as we know it here, not only animal life but plant life included.

PLUTO

Finally we come to the outermost planet Pluto, an extremely faint object discovered only as recently as 1930, and now believed to be roughly much the same size and mass as Mars. Calculations based on further observations after discovery soon revealed a most remarkable peculiarity: its path round the sun was found to link Neptune's (Fig. 31, p. 85), so that although its average distance from the sun was much greater than that of Neptune, yet at times it will have come and will come nearer to the sun. This one apart, all the paths of the planets are quite separate, and with the exception of Mercury are practically concentric circles.

This interlinking of the paths means that at some time in the past, if we go back far enough, Neptune and Pluto must have been very close together, and this has led to the idea that Pluto may be nothing more than an escaped satellite of Neptune and not a genuine planet after all. It can in fact be shown with a fair degree of certainty that the same process that could have ejected Pluto from the Neptunian system could also have reversed the direction of motion of the other satellite, Triton, which has long since made the idea seem very feasible. But certain recent study of Pluto itself makes it look better still, because the rotation period of Pluto has now been found. This requires extremely sensitive equipment because the planet is very faint even by its total light, whereas the method depends on the very small changes of light that it exhibits because of differences of brightness of different parts of its surface as it turns round in regular periodic way. This shows that it rotates in about *six days*, and this is so very long compared with the periods of most of the planets, which rotate in about half a day, that some special influence must have operated to slow it down.

But no such influence is possible on a single planet at such distance from the sun that would not have affected nearer planets far more strongly. However, if it had once been a satellite of Neptune, its period of motion round the planet would very likely be measured in days since that is the kind of rotation period it would have if it always faced its primary. The present satellite, Triton, actually has an orbital period of just under six days. Now it will be recalled that our own moon

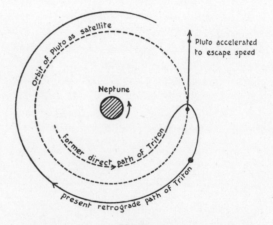

Fig. 33

Triton moves round Neptune the opposite way from the planet's rotation. If both Triton and Pluto were satellites moving in the same forwards direction, the motion of Triton could have been reversed by an encounter with Pluto that also ejected Pluto from the system. Pluto is now an independent planet, but its path round the sun can cross that of Neptune

always presents the same face to the Earth, and therefore has a rotation period equal to its orbital period, namely $27\frac{1}{3}$ days, and that this has been brought about by the back action of the tides on the moon. The same thing is likely to have happened on other planets, and a pretty clear reconstruction can be arrived at of what may have occurred for Neptune. Originally both Triton and Pluto may have been ordinary satellites circling the planet in the same forwards direction; their tidal attractions would by their secondary effects gradually push the satellites further out, but the inner one would recede the faster. Sooner

or later the satellites would be brought sufficiently close together that they would so affect each other's motion that one
was reversed in direction, that would be Triton, and the other
speeded up to such an extent that it escaped from the planet
altogether, and that would be Pluto (Fig. 33).

If this description is correct, and no other explanation has
ever been proposed, it accounts not only for why Pluto rotates
so slowly but why its orbit crosses that of Neptune, and also
why Triton goes round the planet backwards. Nevertheless,
convincing as it seems, all this partakes of the nature of circumstantial evidence, as must almost all theories of past events,
and strong as it is it perhaps does not yet rise to the level of
unquestionable proof. But it is not necessary to make any final
decision: science does not proceed that way. What rather is
done is to say: Here is a certain possible explanation; these
facts seem to bear it out; are there others in favour, are there
any against, and are they fatal objections? The problem always
remains open against new evidence, and until we feel that an
adequate amount of evidence has been obtained we hope for
more, and refrain, or at least try to do so, from making up our
minds that a particular explanation is necessarily the correct
one.

THE MOTIONS OF THE PLANETS

Before saying more about what the solar system contains, it
is necessary to say a little about the actual motions of the
planets. They move, as has already been said, in almost circular
orbits, to be more precise in ellipses with the sun always at one
focus. This is the result of the direct attraction of the sun which
dominates the whole system because of its enormous mass. But
the planets themselves also have mass, and according to
Newton's law of universal gravitation must therefore each exert
a pull on each and every one of the others according to their
sizes and distances apart. The question of predicting in detail
their future paths is thereby rendered extremely complex, but
it can and has been tackled, and with complete success as far as

TABLE OF PLANETARY DATA

	Distance from sun (unit 93 million miles)	Period round sun (years)	Mass Earth=1	Mean radius (miles)	Density (Water=1)	Rotation period	Inclination of equator to path round sun	Number of satellites known
Mercury .	0·387	0·241	0·045	1550	4·1	88 days	?	—
Venus .	·723	·615	·82	3850	4·9	longer than 20 days (?)	?	—
The Earth .	1·0	1·0	1·0	3958·89	5·52	23ʰ 56ᵐ 4ˢ·09	23°·5	1
Mars .	1·524	1·881	·108	2110	3·85	24ʰ 37ᵐ 22ˢ·58	25°·2	2
Ceres (asteroid) .	2·767	4·604	·0001(?)	240	3·3(?)	?	?	—
Jupiter .	5·203	11·862	318·35	43·425	1·33	9ʰ 50ᵐ	3°·1	12
Saturn .	9·539	29·457	95·3	35,800	0·71	10ʰ 14ᵐ	26°·7	9
Uranus .	19·191	84·013	14·6	16,200	1·26	10ʰ 42ᵐ	98°·0	5
Neptune .	30·071	164·783	17·3	15,500	1·61	15ʰ 48ᵐ	29°·0	2
Pluto .	39·518	248·421	0·1(?)	1800(?)	5·7(?)	6 days (?)	?	—

(A question mark means that the value is unknown, or where a value is given that it is uncertain.)

predictions not too far distant in time are concerned. As was mentioned earlier on for instance, eclipses can be predicted to within a matter of seconds of time several years ahead, and this requires highly accurate knowledge of the motion of the Earth round the sun, and of the moon round the Earth; and both these motions are sensibly affected by the other neighbouring planets.

Also the time can be regarded as reversed, and configurations of the planets hundreds or even thousands of years ago worked out with high accuracy. One may wonder therefore why astronomers do not just carry on with the process, backwards in time, and work out just where the planets would finally end up, thereby to discover where they came from. Before the great age of the Earth was realised, this was exactly the plan that the first mathematical astronomers after Newton hoped to carry out. But alas there are difficulties. It appears that although the calculations themselves might be quite trustworthy over a few million years, there would thereafter be mounting unavoidable departures that would finally vitiate them and render them quite invalid for periods as long as one thousand million years. But we have seen that our Earth is far older than this, and so any hope of discovering its origin by purely dynamical considerations, as these are called, is doomed from the outset to failure.

THE ASTEROIDS

But there are other difficulties of a much more straightforward kind, namely the existence in the solar system of many thousands of other small bodies which, though producing negligible effect over short periods of time, would certainly contribute substantially over the whole age of the system. These bodies are the so-called asteroids, and about two thousand of them are now known and are found to be circulating round the sun all in the same general direction as the planets (Fig. 34). The first and what has since proved to be the largest of them was discovered, curiously enough, on the first night of the nineteenth century, 1 January 1801. It was named Ceres, and has a diameter of about 480 miles. It would take ten thousand such bodies to make a planet the size of the Earth. The smallest that have been found are only a mile or two across and are

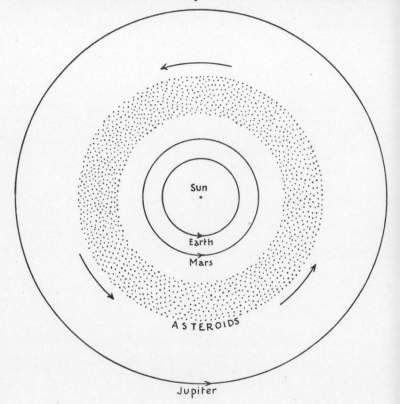

Fig. 34

The asteroids, or minor planets, in relation to the orbits of Mars and Jupiter. About 2,000 of these tiny bodies are known. They all move round the sun in the same general direction as the major planets, but their paths tend to be less circular and more out of the general plane of the planetary system than those of the main planets

quite irregular in shape—"mere mountains broken loose," as one observer described them. There must be far many more still undiscovered, even with available equipment, and Baade estimates that there must be at least thirty thousand discoverable. But worse still there are almost certainly an incomparably greater number much too small ever to be discovered at all unless they happen to pass very near the Earth, or even strike it, when their discovery would not be difficult even if they were only a few feet in size.

This brings us back again to the subject of meteorites, for there can be no doubt that these objects are simply none other than tiny asteroids. So there is the added difficulty, as far as

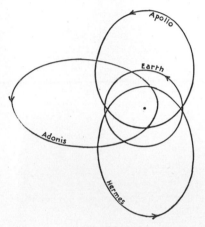

Fig. 35

The orbits of the tiny asteroids Adonis, Apollo, and Hermes at times bring them inside that of the Earth. Their paths are not exactly in one plane. In 1937 Hermes made a record close-approach to the Earth of about 500,000 miles. Collision could eventually occur. Although only a mile or two in size, if one of these struck the Earth it could wipe out a continent

calculations are concerned, of the presence of all these many small bodies whose precise circumstances of motion and mass are quite unknowable, and so no proper allowance can be made for them.

All these considerations go to show how complicated the solar system is, and it is only because the combined weight of asteroids, known and unknown, must be less than a thousandth part of the Earth's weight that calculations of the paths of the planets can be so accurately made for long but nevertheless limited intervals of time. Even so, the combined weight of all the asteroids could well be a million million million tons— enough to produce a million million Arizona craters somewhere in the course of time, if they were all of the same size, which of course they are not.

One may wonder how all these very many bodies can move round the sun without colliding. The eight major planets are of course in pretty circular orbits, and keep to themselves as it were, but as study of the moon shows directly, there is no doubt that many collisions of planets and their satellites with asteroids must have happened in the past and will happen in the future (Fig. 35). These collisions obviously introduce yet another factor rendering it impossible to carry calculations backwards successfully for more than a limited time, because it is impossible to say at what precise moment a collision occurred and what all the conditions were just preceding it.

Not only this, but collisions between asteroids themselves must have happened, and here a fresh consideration enters. For although the collision will produce an explosion of great violence, just as it does if one strikes a full size planet or the moon, the colliding bodies are so small that they will not be able to hold back the resulting fragments, because their force of attraction is negligibly weak. For an object even as large as one hundred miles in diameter, the escape speed at its surface is less than a tenth of a mile per second, whereas some of the velocities produced by the explosion would far exceed this, and the resulting fragments would be scattered into space to give a large number of smaller asteroids. So although the total quantity of asteroidal material must be decreasing the number of asteroids may not necessarily also be doing so, and there may still be countless millions of them moving between the planets. But almost certainly in the earlier stages of the solar system collisions were relatively very frequent, witness the surface of the moon; indeed, the modern trend of views as to the origin of the planets is that they have grown to their present sizes precisely in this way, by the gradual addition of matter at their surfaces through meteoritic bombardment.

COMETS

But there are still more members of the solar system known in the shape of the comets. Not content with the vast array of planets, large and small, circling round the sun, the solar system contains almost certainly at least a hundred thousand other curious objects called comets, very different from planets, and these all move in paths round the sun as well. The traffic

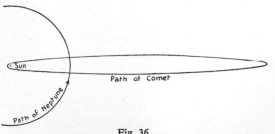

Fig. 36

Path of a comet of intermediate period, about 800 years. Most comets have periods of order 40,000 years, and their paths are far too long and narrow to be drawn on any reasonable scale. Rather more comets move back- wards round the sun than forwards (the planetary direc- tion), and the planes in which they move are almost randomly situated (the reverse of the planets, which all move the same way almost in circles in the same plane)

problem of the solar system may begin to seem serious, but in fact there is plenty of room. Neptune moves at about three thou- sand million miles from the sun, and most of the comets spend by far the greater part of their time moving at distances very much greater than that of Neptune (Fig. 36). About a thousand comets all told have actually been observed to date, but we can be pretty sure that for every *one* that we see there are two or three hundred others in the offing that may ultimately be seen. The reasons for this are simple. Most comets describe highly elongated paths round the sun that take them 40,000 or 50,000 years to complete. But a comet is only visible for a comparatively short time during the small part of its orbit where it sweeps round the sun and is fairly close to the Earth. Even then they are mostly faint telescopic objects, but every year or so there is on average one bright enough to be seen from somewhere on

Earth with unaided eye. And four or five a century are bright enough to be seen in broad daylight without optical aid. There was one in January 1910, and another in December 1927 visible mainly in the southern hemisphere. So there could well be two or three more daylight comets before the present century is out. Now every year on an average three or four new instances of these so-called long-period comets are found, and this has been going on steadily for some centuries. But as each one spends almost all its 40,000 year period, or far longer, out of sight, it follows at once that the total supply of comets must contain well over a hundred thousand.

The arrival of any one of these long-period comets cannot be predicted for the simple reason that the last time it came round must have been some forty thousand or more years ago and man did not trouble to make any observations, at least none that were recorded for posterity. But there is a much smaller number, about one hundred in all, that circulate round the sun at much closer distances in quite short periods, comparable with those of the planets, and so return to view more or less regularly. The most famous comet of all is one of these, namely the great Halley's comet, so called because of the highly important studies of it that Newton's friend Halley carried out. Halley did not discover the comet; indeed, it was seen at several returns by the ancients. The earliest record of its appearance is at least as long ago as 240 B.C., and with less certainty 467 B.C. This is the comet that appeared in the year 1066 at the time of the Battle of Hastings. It last appeared in 1910, and will be round again towards the end of the 1980's (Fig. 37).

A curious thing about comets is that though they are the most negligible things astronomically—even the largest of them if compressed solid would probably make a ball of rock only a mile or two in diameter—they appear to have caused far more terror to superstitious mankind than all the rest of astronomical phenomena put together. Possibly the reason for this is the apparently enormous and sometimes flame-like tails that certain comets—Halley's of course is one—develop when they pass near the sun. The observable part of the tail may extend tens or even hundreds of millions of miles and sometimes reaches across the sky from one horizon to the other. The frequency of comets, as already mentioned, is such that somewhere or other on Earth a comet is visible about once a year to the unaided eye, and as political or similar catastrophes were

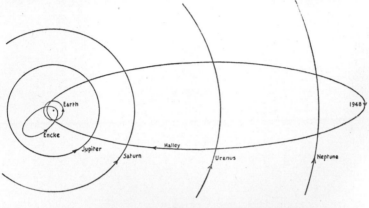

Fig. 37

The paths of Halley's comet and Encke's comet. (They lie in planes inclined at about 18° and 12° respectively to the Earth's orbit plane.) Encke's comet has the shortest period, 3·28 years, of all known comets. The orbit of Halley's comet is retrograde. Its last closest approach to the sun was in 1910, and its next will be about the year 1986 when it will probably again become visible even to the unaided eye. The comet was at its furthest from the sun in 1948

scarcely less frequent in the past than today, there was plenty of scope for attributing national calamities to the influence of comets. Until comparatively recent times their appearance was widely regarded as a portent of impending evil. Shakespeare has Caesar's wife Calphurnia warning him shortly before his assassination with the words "Fierce fiery warriors fight upon the clouds"—there was a comet in the heavens at the time—and she went on with the famous lines "When beggars die there are no comets seen, The heavens themselves blaze forth the death of princes."

When we come to ask what a comet is, what it is really like, and what it is made of if it has so little mass and yet so great a size, there is some difficulty in deciding. The usual photographs that are taken of comets do not really show at all what the head is like, because comet photographers mainly prefer to get a good exposure to show the tail, which generally is much fainter than the comet, and so the head tends to be over-exposed and made to look as if it were perfectly round and uniformly bright. But really a comet is not at all like that. Fig. 38 shows some sketches of what the head of Halley's comet looked like at different times at its last return. What these sketches obviously show is that there is no definite recognisable form at all, and that a comet's head changes in its details from day to day, if not even from hour to hour. In this way comets are very

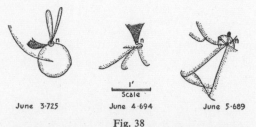

June 3·725   June 4·694   June 5·689

Fig. 38

Sketches by Bobrovnikoff of formations within the head of Halley's comet at three instants about 24 hours apart during its 1910 return. The circles and lines (shown dark) represent expanding luminous shells and jets emanating mainly from the nucleus *n*. The detailed appearance of the comet changes rapidly and shows no settled structure at all. (The instants are given as decimals of the day)

different from planets, which are quite unchanging in form and instantly recognisable from their appearance; no one could confuse Mars with Jupiter. But this is not so for comets, and the only way it is known that it is the same Halley's comet, for instance, that returns every seventy-seven years or so, is because it comes precisely at the expected time and in precisely the right path; so it must be the same comet.

When a comet approaches the sun it undergoes curiously unexpected changes. Besides the flaring out of the tail, which always points more or less directly away from the sun, trailing behind as the comet approaches and running on ahead as it recedes, like the smoke of a steamer in a following wind (Fig. 39), the head of the comet contracts, whereas one might have expected the heat of the sun rather to produce the reverse effect and expand the comet. Also a comet often undergoes the strangest

internal contortions as though it were writhing about. Mean-
while the comet as a whole steadily pursues its path round the
sun. These extraordinary properties of comets were known to
Leonardo da Vinci over four centuries ago, but comets are not
very fashionable subjects of study today and few modern
astronomers appear to know as much about them as did Leonardo. Here is what he said: "Why this comet seems variable

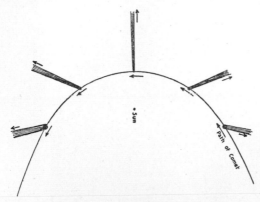

Fig. 39

The tail always streams away from the comet in the
direction more or less opposite to that of the sun. As
the comet approaches the sun the tail streams away
behind, and as the comet recedes the tail runs on
ahead. The tail forms only during a limited part of the
path while the comet is sweeping round the sun, as
indicated

in shape, so that at one time it is round, at another long,
at another divided into two or three parts, at another united,
and sometimes invisible and sometimes becoming visible
again."

Now it is quite clear that no ordinary solid body could behave like this, and to cut a long and fascinating story short what
has been established is that a comet consists of a huge swarm
of tiny dust particles no bigger than grains of sand spaced
yards apart from each other, and the whole thing occupying an
enormous volume. Holmes's comet of 1892 for instance had a
general extent greater in volume than the sun though it would
have less than one thousand-million-millionth of the sun's mass.
The particles are so widely spaced that the comet as a whole

is completely transparent, and stars lying beyond in the line of sight from the Earth can be seen undimmed right through the head of the comet. Again, when in 1910 Halley's comet passed directly between the Earth and the sun, it became completely invisible as it passed across the disc of the sun, though it was known exactly where it must be at each stage, and the same thing has happened with other comets.

When a comet gets near the sun all these myriads of small particles—resembling a giant swarm of gnats—move quite independently of each other, because the attractive forces due to the comet as a whole are so weak compared with those due to the sun, and analysis shows that it is this feature that brings about these strange changes of shape. If the swarm is quite irregular, although of course more or less localised, it is understandable that rapid changes may produce very strange temporary forms, and it is apparent changes resulting from this sort of thing and seen more or less at the limit of vision that Leonardo must have observed.

During all these changes some of the particles forming the comet will collide with each other, and thereby produce still smaller particles merely by the disruptive effect of the collisions. In this way very fine dust will be formed within the comet, and at this stage a most surprising effect enters and takes charge. If a piece of matter is small enough, the pressure of light falling on it can become a highly effective force. The particles must have sizes of the order of the wavelength of light for this force to rise to importance—the wavelengths of light from the sun are of the order of a few hundred-thousandths of an inch—and particles of these sizes produced in the comet would immediately be repelled directly away from the sun by the light pressure exerted on them and go to form the tail. They are lost forever from the comet, but represent such a small part of the total mass that a comet can go on producing tail after tail at each successive approach to the sun for thousands of years, as Halley's comet is known to have done. Huge as the dimensions of a tail may be, at any one instant it may contain only a few tons of matter, so rarefied and finely divided is it and so great its reflecting power mass for mass in this state.

METEORS

Now another effect of these changes as the comet approaches the sun is that particles within it and colliding with each other thereby receive small changes of velocity. Imagine people brushing past each other in the corridor of an express train; it does not alter their general motions much, and they still go forward with the train. But in the case of the comet all the particles are moving freely in space, they are not encased in any

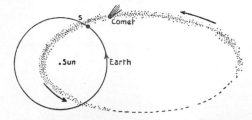

Fig. 40
Passage of the Earth through a meteor stream
Associated with a comet there may be a stream of widely spaced tiny particles moving ahead and behind the comet with practically the same motion. In some cases the stream is spread right round the orbit. If the Earth's path takes it through the stream as at S, then at that time of year particles are intercepted by the Earth's atmosphere to become visible as meteors. A meteor shower so produced may last several days. The particles in the stream are smaller than grains of sand and may be hundreds of miles apart. Meteor streams also exist for which there is no (longer any) associated comet

way, and the slight speedings-up and retardings that some of the particles receive must alter their orbits slightly, particularly the time they take to circuit the sun. Some therefore gradually run on ahead of the comet and others lag behind. In the course of time a great stream of particles forms in this way, extending along the path of the comet; in some cases they are known to extend right the way round, so that the comet itself is a kind of condensation or concentration of particles remaining at one part of this long stream (Fig. 40). The stream itself can be visualised rather like a gigantic vapour-trail extending along the path of the comet, except that the trail is not formed of water droplets but of tiny solid particles, most of them no bigger than breadcrumbs.

Now it may happen that the path of the comet is such that this huge tubular stream of dust particles is met at one or perhaps two places by the Earth's orbit. In that case if the stream happens to be there, like a train crossing a level-crossing, when the Earth is describing that part of its orbit round the sun (which will of course happen at a particular time of year), the Earth will have to plough its way through this stream of tiny particles. But there is no danger, the little particles will be hundreds of miles apart, and though they may be approaching the Earth with speeds of anything up to nearly fifty miles a second, the air over our heads is a perfect shield from them. These are the shooting-stars, a few of which can always be seen if one watches the sky for half an hour or so on any dark clear night. Technically they are termed *meteors*, but are not to be confused with meteorites, which as has been explained are much larger objects to be thought of rather as small asteroids.

What happens to the meteor on striking the Earth's atmosphere is that it moves so fast through the upper layers of air that friction renders it brilliantly incandescent, and it is the luminous trail that it leaves behind that is actually seen. Meteors never reach ground level but burn themselves right away at a height of some sixty to eighty miles above the Earth's surface. Early August is now the best time of year for meteors as a rule, though at one time November was the best month. The most intense display ever seems to have occurred in the year 1833 in November, when it was estimated that about two hundred thousand meteors an hour could be seen from a single place. The sky is described as having been like a hail-storm with them, but not a single one was found to penetrate down to ground level. It is now known that many thousand millions of meteors each day enter the Earth's atmosphere, in sizes right down to the smallest capable of producing any effect. By modern radio means they can be detected equally well in broad daylight, and innumerable new streams round the sun have been found that otherwise might have remained undiscovered indefinitely. It has been established that many of these meteor streams are moving round the sun in exactly the same paths as are followed by well-known comets, and it now seems probable that almost all meteors move in such paths. Also, radio-equipment will detect meteors that are much too faint to be seen visually.

All this source of wastage and gradual destruction of comets is going on continually, but a far greater destructive effect is the gradual drawing in to the sun of the particles of the stream and of the comet itself as a result of the sun's light. Whereas the infinitesimal particles of the tail are driven away into outer space, the present effect now causes the heavier, but still very small particles to spiral gradually towards the sun, where they are first vaporised and then absorbed into its atmosphere before eventually becoming mixed right into the deep interior of the sun. The comets, being made of dust, are formed principally of heavy elements, and this mechanism may be of considerable importance to the sun and stars, because these bodies need a small amount of heavy elements in them to operate some of the processes that produce their light and heat. For this reason comets may turn out to be specially important objects, and also very beneficent, if they play this special role in the working of the system. It is almost certainly the case that a large proportion of other stars have just as many comets circling round them, and it may perhaps be estimated that to every star in the universe there are roughly 100,000 comets. As there are 100,000,000,000 stars in our galaxy alone, that is in our Milky Way system, there seems little doubt that comets form by far the most numerous class of observable astronomical objects.

So when you next see a shooting-star speed across the sky, do not suppose that some celestial tragedy has happened, and a full-sized star fallen from grace. It is only a tiny grain, no larger than a breadcrumb, but allowed to shine for a brief moment with all the glory of a real star, before destroying itself in the effort and vanishing for ever.

REFERENCES

Astronomy, Vol. I, H. N. Russell, Ginn & Co., 1945.

Life on Other Worlds, H. Spencer Jones, Macmillan, 1940.

Between the Planets, F. G. Watson, Blakiston Co., 1941.

The Comets and Their Origin, R. A. Lyttleton, Cambridge, 1953.

Meteors, C. P. Olivier, Williams and Wilkins, Baltimore, 1925.

Comets and Meteor Streams, J. G. Porter, Chapman and Hall, 1952.

IV

THE SUN

The sun a star—Surface conditions—Rotation
—Darkening at limb—Light emitted—Source
of energy—Age of sun—Future life—Sunspots—
Sunspot cycle—Irregularities—Spectroscope—
Magnetic field of sunspots—Emission of ultra-
violet light and particles—Eclipses and the Corona
—Zodiacal light—Theories of corona—Promin-
ences—Interior conditions—Luminosity and
Radius related to Mass and Composition—Only
Helium built up in sun—Data for sun.

OUR NEAREST STAR

We must all at some time or other have wondered what the stars are like, even apart from our irresolute recital in early childhood of "Twinkle, twinkle, little star, How I wonder what you are." One might suppose that if only we could get near enough then we could have a real look at a star, but there is great difficulty about this, for the nearer we get the more impossible it becomes to look at a star. There is, in fact, a star quite as comfortably close as we can put up with in the shape of our own sun, and everyone knows how difficult (and indeed dangerous) it is to look at in a clear sky on a summer's day, despite the immense distance of ninety-three million miles separating us from it.

All the stars we see in the sky are simply other suns, as also are all the very great many others that cannot be seen at all except with powerful telescopes. Some are thousands of times brighter than the sun in their total light and others a good deal fainter. The sun is simply the nearest of the stars, a vast incandescent sphere of gas—there is no solid surface anywhere —some 864,000 miles in diameter and at tremendously high temperature. Though only of medium size and brightness when compared with other stars, yet it is enormous in size compared with the Earth or with any of the planets that move round it. It is the sun's attraction that controls their motions. Also the sun is unique in being the one star in the universe for which it is possible to study the details of its surface. All the others are so remote that no telescope yet constructed can show them as more than mere points of light.

The sun is not only the most splendid in appearance of all the objects in the heavens, but to ourselves it is by far the most important. We see it rise and set each day, and shine with superlative brilliance, and it provides us with a regular supply of light and heat on which we are utterly and absolutely dependent. Yet we are so accustomed to this bounty that we are apt to take it for granted and forget that even the daylight, which seems to come equally from all parts of the sky, is really due solely to the sun. Indeed when Alexis Tolstoy's civil servant Prutkov was asked, "Which is the more useful, the sun or the moon?" he replied without hesitation "The moon, of course, because it gives a little light at night, when it is dark; whereas the sun only shines in the daytime, when it is light anyway!"

Now because the sun's light is so intense—every square inch of its surface shines with a brilliance of 300,000 candlepower—astronomers have had to devise other ways of looking at it than direct ones which would almost blind them in the process. One of the simplest methods is to pass the sunlight through the magnifying lenses of a telescope and allow the resulting rays to form an image of the sun on a white screen, which can then be examined and watched with complete safety to the eyes. Alternatively, the image can be allowed to fall on a photographic plate, when the shortest of exposures gives a permanent picture of the sun's outer surface at the instant concerned. Frequent pictures of the sun are obtained in this way, at many observatories, weather permitting, and they enable a more or less continuous day to day record of detailed conditions at the surface to be built up that can be studied and referred back to thereafter at leisure.

The sun appears in the first place as a brilliantly luminous sphere of white light, termed the *photosphere*. This surface from which the light comes is at a temperature of about 6000° C.—about twice as hot as an electric light filament. This seems hot enough in all conscience, but it is as nothing compared with the several millions of degrees far down inside the sun. It is in fact this great difference of temperature that drives out the enormous flood of radiant energy from the deep interior, where it is produced, through hundreds of thousands of miles of opaque material, eventually to reach the free surface and take off for its journey across space.

You will have noticed how perfectly spherical the sun is. Its rotation, unlike that of many of the planets, is far too slow to cause any noticeable flattening. Measurements of the motions of sunspots show that near its equator the sun takes about twenty-five days to turn round once, but that it moves round more and more slowly as we go towards the poles. In other . words, that the sun does not rotate uniformly, as it would if it were a rigid body (Fig. 41). The internal rotation rates can only

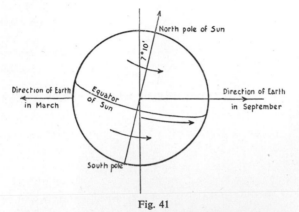

Fig. 41

The axis of rotation of the sun is not upright, but lies over at a small angle of about 7 degrees. In September the north pole of the sun is visible from the Earth, and in March the south pole is visible. At the equator the sun rotates in about 25 days, but it rotates more slowly with increasing latitude

ever be assessed by theoretical methods and at present are not known with any real certainty. According to Jeans, requirements of radiation transport suggest that the central parts may rotate about nine times as quickly as the visible outer parts.

But the idea of the sun being a sphere of light at a definite temperature is only the simplest description of what is really a most complex object even so far as its surface properties go. One of the most striking features that photographs reveal is the way the sun appears darker area for area the nearer we approach to the rim. This is not an illusion, but is due to the fact that at these parts the light has to make its way out through more atmosphere (Fig. 42). Put another way, we can see deeper into the sun at the centre of its disc where we are looking straight down through the atmosphere, and therefore to a level where it is hotter, than near the edge where we are looking almost parallel to the surface. This effect is obviously greater the nearer the limb of the sun we look, and accordingly it appears progressively darker towards the edge.

Now this level in the sun that we can see down to at the centre of the disc is at a temperature of nearly six thousand degrees centigrade, more than twice as hot as any blast furnace, and this is the temperature of the regions of the outer layers from which actually comes most of the light by which we

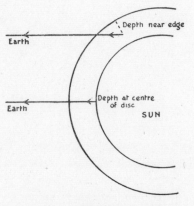

Fig. 42
Darkening at the limb of the sun. Showing how at the centre of the sun's disc the light comes from greater depth where the temperature is higher than it does near the edge. The sun accordingly looks brighter, area for area, at the centre than near the edge

eventually see the sun. So intense is the flow of heat at the surface that every square inch is sending out energy at the rate of nearly sixty horsepower, and as the sun's surface area is about twelve thousand times that of the whole Earth, this gives an idea how large is the total energy output. Although this radiant energy has not got material form, it nevertheless possesses mass. All forms of energy have mass, but for the amounts of energy we ourselves deal with on Earth it is always negligibly small, and this led to its being overlooked until comparatively recent times. But the total weight of the light leaving the sun every second is over four million tons. The Earth itself is so small and so far away that it intercepts only four pounds weight per second of the whole vast escaping stream of light. This may not seem very much, but light is travelling at 186,000 miles a second, and at that speed four pounds of light possesses a very great deal of energy.

It is now known that the sun's energy comes ultimately from the conversion of hydrogen into helium deep down in the most central parts of the sun. The necessary rate of conversion is at six hundred million tons per second. This weight of hydrogen is accordingly consumed every second of time and transmuted into 596 million tons of helium and 4 million tons of light, in round numbers. The sun has been doing this, and thereby keeping at very much the same brightness, for something like five or six thousand million years. But even so it has used up less than ten per cent of its whole store of hydrogen. As can be imagined it must therefore have enormous total weight by ordinary standards, and in fact it actually weighs, in round numbers, two thousand million million million million tons, that is 2×10^{27} tons.

It used to be a great mystery how the sun kept going, for it was quite clear that it could be no ordinary kind of fire that was responsible for its heat. If the sun were made of coal and were burning so as to give out the present amount of light and heat, it would be reduced to ashes in a very few thousand years. But the Earth is about a million times as old as this, and all the evidence shows that the sun has been shining on it throughout quite as strongly as it still does. No ordinary chemical processes could keep up the supply so long; it requires sub-atomic energy, nuclear energy. The sun is an atomic energy powerhouse in a really big way of business, but it has the process under complete control, with beautifully simple means to turn off the heat a little if things go too fast, and to step it up if they go too slowly. This state of affairs has persisted for several thousand million years, and we can confidently expect the sun to go on shining for several thousands of millions of years more before any possible fuel shortage overtakes it. Indeed, there may even be opportunities from time to time for the sun to refuel itself by picking up more hydrogen as it moves along through space and occasionally encounters large diffuse clouds of interstellar hydrogen.

SUNSPOTS

At more or less irregular times conspicuous dark markings break out on the otherwise perfect solar surface. These are the famous sunspots, some of which are large enough to be visible to the unaided (but should not be unscreened) eye. Ancient Chinese records contain many references to sunspots, some nearly two thousand years ago, but systematic study of them began only in 1610 with the invention of the telescope. A normal spot consists of a dark central region, the *umbra*, surrounded by a less dark border, the *penumbra*, composed of filaments that appear to converge into the spot. The umbra is not always uniformly dark, at times appearing somewhat veiled by filmy clouds, but few spots are ever strictly normal in type, rather like people. There is a strong tendency for groups of spots to form, surrounded by a common penumbra.

The spots are gigantic disturbances that form in the solar atmosphere, but how far they extend below is as yet quite unknown. A number of theories have been propounded though they are all far from satisfactory. At one end of the scale some theories consider the spots to be an entirely superficial phenomenon confined to the very outermost layers, while at the other end there are theories that assign their cause to the deepest central parts of the sun, hundreds of thousands of miles below the surface, with the spots the merest surface evidence of far stronger internal disturbances. Sunspots range in size from about five hundred miles across for the smallest that can be seen to anything up to fifty thousand miles for the very largest. A large group of spots may measure far more than a hundred thousand miles across. The temperature in a spot is much lower than elsewhere on the surface, about four thousand degrees centigrade, instead of nearly six thousand at the undisturbed parts. But the spots only look dark by comparison with the surrounding regions; in fact they are still brilliantly luminous, though considerably less so area for area than the general surface of course.

Now the curious thing is that these spots are by no means long-lived features. No spot is permanent. They usually take a few days to develop fully, but sometimes only hours, appearing gradually at parts of the surface that hitherto showed no unusual signs. Thereafter they seem slowly to be reabsorbed into the surrounding parts, taking several days or even weeks to disappear, the larger ones in general lasting longer—the record is about eighteen months. All this takes place in a more or less irregular way as far as any local region of the sun is concerned, but superposed on this irregularity a kind of periodicity that is almost perfectly regular has been found for the sun as a whole. If the number of visible spots, or their total area, during each month, say, is recorded and a graph made of these numbers with time, then over the years a well-defined almost periodic curve is found to be obtained. The number rises and falls systematically with a general period of just over eleven years on average, though on occasion it has been as short as seven years, and as long as seventeen years. This whole course of development during each eleven-year period is called the *sunspot cycle*.

The beginning of a cycle is usually regarded as the time when no spots at all are forming on the surface, and when the fresh cycle starts the new spots appear only in fairly high latitudes on the solar surface, that is at regions some 30° to 35° north and south, seldom more, of the equator—for the sun the equator is defined as for the Earth by the rotation axis, being the circle ninety degrees away from the polar points of the surface where this axis meets it (Fig. 41). Then as the cycle proceeds from year to year the places where new spots form gradually approach the equator, until towards the end of the eleven-year cycle such few spots as still form tend to break out at places not far north and south of the equator. At this stage the beginnings of the next cycle may start to show by minor outbreaks of spots again in high latitudes (30°-35°) north and south, so that at such times there are four zones where spots are likely to occur, though this is at a stage when spots are in any case rare. Few spots ever occur further north (or south) than about 35°, or nearer the sun's equator than about 5° north (or south), so that in addition to the polar areas (beyond latitudes ± 40°) there is an equatorial belt several degrees wide in which spots are almost never to be found. In all, the spots are confined to just over half the area of the sun.

Apart from this general cyclic change, the curious feature has emerged from the records that the southern hemisphere has shown nearly 20% more spots than the northern half taken over this past eighty years. Still more strange, perhaps, spots stopped appearing almost completely between 1640 and 1716, and another spell when they were very rare came between 1798 and 1833.

Why the sunspot cycle happens, and these other curious departures from it, is still a complete mystery, but the procession of events is followed out faithfully in each succeeding cycle, and has now been observed in detail for the best part of a century. Part of the difficulty undoubtedly is that even the sun's undisturbed atmosphere is still only very imperfectly understood as to the main forces and processes involved in it. But please do not suppose that this is due to any special mental incapacity on the part of astronomers. Everyone knows when it comes to the weather how little is understood for certain about our own atmosphere, in which the meteorologists like ourselves actually live and can examine it at first hand. So it is perhaps not surprising that the sun's weather—for this is how sunspots can be thought of—is going to be difficult to explain and understand.

THE SPECTROSCOPE

Now there is another way of studying the sun, and indeed the stars generally, which is of tremendous power and importance, and that is by means of an optical device called a spectroscope. When a beam of light passes through a prism of glass it is split into its fundamental colours. In the case of sunlight these are the colours of the rainbow. But if the beam of light is first sent through a sufficiently narrow slit, the overlapping of adjacent colours is obviated and a whole series of individual separated narrow beams of light are obtained, each capable of giving an image of the slit at and near every wave-length, and corresponding to a much finer subdivision of the original light (Fig. 43). The images of these various narrow beams on a

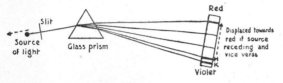

Fig. 43

The spectroscope. Light passed through a narrow slit and a glass prism is dispersed into its primary colours; the image of the slit shows itself as "lines." For sunlight the colours are those of the rainbow, ranging from red to violet, and dark lines appear superposed on these produced by absorption in the sun's outer atmosphere. If the source is receding these lines are displaced towards the red, and if it is approaching towards the violet, by amounts depending on the speed and the particular colour. If the source is in a strong magnetic field the resulting lines may be doubled or tripled according to the direction of the field

screen or photographic plate are called *lines*, and the whole system of lines due to a given source of light is called a *spectrum*. The discovery of these lines has been one of the most important steps in the development of modern science, providing as they do a vast amount of evidence intimately related to the atomic structure of matter and its deep connection with light. This resolution of light into its primary colours was effected by Newton, but unhappily he did not chance to make use of the simple expedient of a slit, and so remained unaware of the existence of the individual *spectral* lines. With his great intellect, had he only had the good fortune to produce the lines, the development of science and the whole history of mankind from that time on would have been different, since well over a century was to pass before the lines were found and their implications as to the structure of matter begun to be considered.

The various lines in the spectrum of an object such as the sun correspond to different substances in the sun's atmosphere, and all this can be verified directly in the laboratory where the lines can be reproduced in detail and the conditions for their production found. It is possible to screen off all the lines coming from a given light-source except one and thereby take a photograph in just one wavelength. In this way the sun can be photographed in a single line of hydrogen, or in calcium, for instance, and other elements. The spectroscope discloses the actual composition of the sun at the layers where the light finally comes from, and what is found is that almost all known elements are present in small amounts, but that hydrogen and helium are immensely abundant, with hydrogen far exceeding all the rest put together. It must be emphasised that this refers only to the very outermost layers, which contain but an insignificant proportion of the sun's entire mass, and at this stage it must not be supposed that the composition of the deep interior is necessarily the same as what we actually see at the surface, any more than it is valid to suppose that chimney-sweeps are made throughout of soot. But fortunately there are other ways, necessarily theoretical, of getting to know the internal composition, and these confirm that hydrogen and helium are the two main substances, with hydrogen providing at least ninety per cent of the whole, and the two together making up at least ninety-eight per cent.

THE MAGNETIC FIELD OF SUNSPOTS

Now besides the power of revealing the elements that are emitting the light, these spectral lines have other very remarkable properties. If the light is being given out in the region of a powerful magnetic field, such for instance as could be produced here on Earth between the poles of a powerful electromagnet, then an individual line may be doubled or even tripled according to the relation of the magnetic field to the direction of the light. That is, where normally a single line might appear, there now appear two or three lines in positions slightly displaced from the standard position of the original single line. This is known as the Zeeman effect, after the Dutch physicist of that name, and it makes it readily possible to detect magnetic fields not only on the sun but at much remoter parts of the universe.

In this way it has been established that sunspots have powerful magnetic fields associated with them; their strengths run up to anything like three or four thousand gauss (the *gauss* is a unit of magnetic force), which means several thousand times the Earth's field strength (which is rather less than one gauss even at its strongest parts). The fields in spots compare with the fields between the poles of a strong electromagnet, which with a sufficiently strong electric current can be produced over a few square feet. But in sunspots this intensity is maintained for days or even weeks on end over an area of several hundred million square miles, so it is clear that vast amounts of energy are involved in producing them.

Besides simply the presence of magnetic fields in sunspots, there are certain striking peculiarities of their arrangement both in adjacent spots and in the two opposite hemispheres. Associated with magnetism there are always two polarities, north and south, and at any place in a magnetic field the force is directed always as though it were flowing out of either a north pole or a south pole. Now it is found that for a pair of spots for which the whirling motions are opposite, the magnetic fields coming up out of them are also opposite. Moreover in a group of sunspots consisting of two major spots, the leading one (the right hand one if the sun's north pole is regarded as uppermost) has the opposite polarity from the following one. And in the same cycle a similar spot-pair in the opposite hemisphere not only also has opposite polarities for its two members, but these are now the other way round. Throughout any one cycle the leading spot of such pairs always has the same polarity, but opposite in the two hemispheres, and this polarity is reversed in the next cycle. This change of polarity has now been observed to take place for five successive cycles since its initial discovery, and this had led to the sunspot period being regarded rather as twenty-two years instead of the straightforward eleven years exhibited simply by the spots themselves. But in the absence of any explanation of either the spots or their magnetic fields, there is nothing to be gained in regarding either period as the more preferable. It could even be the case, as far as anything is yet known, that the reversal of polarity will not happen for some future new cycle, we just cannot be sure in the absence of an understanding of the whole phenomenon, and this is very far from having been achieved.

EMISSION OF ULTRA-VIOLET LIGHT AND PARTICLES FROM THE SUN

At certain regions of the sun's surface brilliant clouds, termed flares, are found suddenly to send out many times their normal emission of energy, particularly in hydrogen light. Besides ordinary visible wave-lengths, such regions send out strong ultra-violet light that causes intense effects (ionisation) in the Earth's atmosphere, which disturb long-distance radio communications, and cause small irregular magnetic effects.

The same regions of the sun also emit charged particles at speeds of the order of a thousand miles a second. These particles are fired out from the solar surface rather like a stream from a gigantic hose that the rotation of the sun causes to sweep across the position of the Earth. The particles arrive a day or two later than does the ultra-violet light from the same region, and they not only show their arrival indirectly by causing magnetic and ionospheric storms in the Earth's atmosphere, but in a sense actually make themselves visible by producing *aurorae* in the high atmosphere.

ECLIPSES AND THE CORONA

Now, besides all these remarkable properties, the sun has yet another surprise in store for us, and one that might never have been found out but for the happy and harmless accident of total eclipses. At such times the moon's disc more than covers that of the sun and cuts off from view the whole of the dazzling region—the photosphere—where the light is normally seen to come from. At the moment this stage is first reached during an eclipse, a marvellously unexpected thing happens and a brilliantly luminous atmosphere surrounding the sun, otherwise totally invisible, suddenly flashes out, extending in some directions by several solar diameters. This vision is the famous *solar corona*. It is principally in order to study and photograph the corona that observational astronomers travel thousands of miles, after spending months or years preparing their equipment, to take advantage of the very few minutes of totality that an eclipse may allow.

By means of photographs taken at many different eclipses it has been found that the corona is by no means always of the same shape. In fact it tends to follow a regular series of forms through the sunspot cycle, being always of more or less the same shape at the same stage of each particular cycle. There is a so-called *minimum*-type corona, which is typical of sunspot minimum when the number of spots may be almost zero, and in it the corona extends far out from the sun in equatorial regions, while at the polar regions it is sharply defined but visible only very close to the sun's surface. On the other hand there is a quite differently shaped corona of *maximum*-type that extends out much the same in all directions and so is more or less symmetrical all round the sun. Eclipses occurring between the two times reveal that the corona changes gradually from one to the other and back again regularly with the sunspot cycle.

By delicate intensity measurements the corona can be detected extending out far beyond the distances that photographs ordinarily show. For instance at the eclipse of 30 June 1954, which was right at the middle of the most recent sunspot minimum, the equatorial extensions could easily be detected out to about eight solar diameters on the eastern side of the sun and to about six diameters on the western side, while at earlier eclipses the corona has been found to possess even greater extension.

At large distances the coronal brightness is likely to be extremely weak compared with the general background light of the sky especially for observations at ground-level. But recent measures from a high-level aircraft during total eclipse have succeeded in detecting the corona out to distances beyond fifty solar radii (about a quarter of the way out from the sun to the Earth), as a result of which it is now even claimed that the corona may extend continuously to the *zodiacal light* itself. The existence of this latter phenomenon has long been known; it shows itself as a weak band of light, faintly visible on extremely dark but clear nights, extending round the Earth and lying close to the general plane in which the planets move round the sun. Near the horizon it appears broader and brighter than parts of the Milky Way itself, but it becomes narrower and fainter with increasing altitude.

Apart from its mere existence, one of the most extraordinary features of the corona is that the material of which it is formed is at unexpectedly high temperature, at places much exceeding a million degrees. This can be inferred from certain lines in its spectrum (obtained during total eclipses), which can only be produced if the material has such a temperature.

THEORIES OF THE CORONA

These exciting discoveries have naturally brought in their train a good deal of speculation as to what the corona is formed of and what conditions in it must be like, and above all how it originates at all. In the main ideas divide into two kinds. According to one, the material forming the corona is expelled outwards from the sun itself and must therefore be regarded as something intrinsic to the sun. The high temperature of the material might be accounted for by supposing that it came from far down in the sun, but how or why such material at a million degrees could push its way through the cooler layers, at a mere few thousand degrees, overlying it without itself becoming cooled has never been explained. Another suggestion is that the high temperature is itself generated in the sun's outer atmosphere (below the corona) by shock waves, but the source of energy required for this to happen has not been identified.

The other view, which let it be said at the outset seems much more tenable, is that the corona represents material *falling* in towards the solar surface, and so assigns the cause of the corona to something entirely external to the sun (Fig. 44). The balance of evidence certainly favours this second idea strongly, and moreover there are available definite sources of the necessary material and the energy. Nevertheless, curiously enough, many astronomers cling to the internal theory despite the paucity even of circumstantial evidence favouring it, and in face of a good deal of direct evidence supporting the infall theory. As

Fig. 44

Illustrating the infall theory of the solar corona

Far out the material is flowing inwards under the sun's powerful attraction, but nearer in it is churning *up* and *down* very violently as a result of adjustments at the surface necessary to accommodate the very high energy of infall carried by the material

will be explained more fully in the next chapter, the space between the stars is by no means completely void, but contains very tenuous clouds, mainly of hydrogen, that a star such as our sun may overtake, or be overtaken by, with the result that from time to time it may find itself surrounded by a vast cloud of hydrogen at extremely low density—far too low for its presence to be detected directly. There is no reason to suppose that the sun is not moving through such a cloud now. If so, its attraction must draw the material inwards, and the theory is that the corona we see is simply this material more and more compressed (but still very very tenuous) as it finally reaches the sun. The high temperature is explicable also in terms of the energy of infall, though not quite directly, since any object falling to the sun's surface would have a speed when it gets there of about four hundred miles a second. The inner part of the corona where the temperature is so great owes its properties to the adjustment that the outer atmosphere of the sun has to make to receive this infalling high-speed material, whereas far out the corona represents simply the incoming material itself.

It is not at present possible to settle finally which of these theories, if either, is correct, but it may become so soon if, for instance, means can be devised to determine the direction of motion—towards or away from the sun—sufficiently far out in the corona. The infall type of theory also holds out some hope of throwing light on both the sunspot phenomenon and the associated magnetic fields. If the interstellar material carries with it a weak magnetic field, this is likely to become enormously intensified as a result of the general compression produced through the infall to the sun, and the solar atmosphere, which is itself very tenuous, would not only have to adjust itself to receive this material, but at the same time satisfy all the thermal and mechanical requirements that its own permanent conditions, such as temperature, density, and rotation, impose. It would be a bold decision to say that out of such complex conditions sunspots and their magnetic fields could not result, though equally so it is a far cry from asserting that this has yet been established. It also seems very suggestive that the sunspot period, although irregular, so nearly equals that of Jupiter (11·86 years) in his orbit round the sun, though it may of course be pure coincidence. Jupiter, because of his great mass, would be most effective in disturbing any inflow of material to the sun, if only by his displacement of the general centre of attraction (on material at a great distance) to a point no longer coinciding with the centre of the sun. Furthermore, if interstellar material is supplying the substance of the corona, and the infalling corona is in turn producing the sunspots, it would be easy to see how the latter could temporarily cease, or almost do so, if the sun happened to pass through a region of space almost devoid of interstellar material, and this could occur more or less irregularly over the years.

PROMINENCES

As eclipses by the moon allow something like one minute per year on the average for observation of the corona, astronomers have naturally been driven to trying to produce artificial eclipses by screening the sun with a disc, rather than go on waiting on the moon's caprice and after all their efforts being then so much at the mercy of the weather. The difficulty is of course to get rid of the light scattered by our own atmosphere from the strong sunlight entering it. But this has been successfully overcome at certain high-altitude observatories, and it is nowadays possible to photograph the bright inner corona, and even to film the changes going on in it just above the sun's surface.

One of the most impressive features so revealed are the *prominences* which often have the appearance of gigantic luminous arches ranging up to anything like a hundred thousand miles in extent. Occasionally prominences are seen at times of ordinary total eclipses. Although highly luminous, it now seems likely that the prominences are *cooler* regions that can emit light within a surrounding much hotter atmosphere, that is at too high a temperature for as much light to be emitted by it, so that the actual situation may be the reverse of what might first be supposed.

Most if not all prominences seem to be associated with newly formed sunspots. There are all sorts of typical forms to be seen, looking like arches, ropes, ribbons, and knots, and at times quite irregularly shaped condensations. Filaments point more or less towards spots and sometimes seem to be drawn in towards them. Some of the upward surges are of really explosive violence. But on the whole there seems to be a preponderance of downward motions. There are also indications that strong magnetic forces may be influencing the motions, but the conditions are obviously extremely complex. The speeds associated with the apparent motions are to be measured in hundreds of miles a second, but it is difficult to be certain, with movements of this kind that are seen only across the line of sight (not along it towards or away from the observer), whether what is observed is an actual motion of material, or merely the transmission of an effect through material not necessarily moving in the way seen at all. An example of such an apparent motion is provided by a searchlight beam playing across stationary clouds; this gives the appearance of something in rapid motion across the sky, but it is not a material motion, and it can change suddenly and discontinuously, as these motions near the surface of the sun are often seen to do.

THE INTERIOR OF THE SUN

When it comes to the interior of the sun we are concerned with a region no longer accessible to direct observation at all. But this does not imply that it is beyond the resources of science to discover the prevailing conditions by any means. It is now necessary, however, to rely on what are really the most important and powerful weapons of all in unravelling the secrets of the universe, namely those of the human intellect, imagination and ingenuity. The principal data that we have to go upon are simple and reliable enough. We know in the first place that somehow the interior is producing the great flood of radiation that streams out at the surface, and we know both the total weight and the size of the sun. Added to this, a great deal is now known about how matter behaves under conditions of extremely high temperature; this has been discovered mainly as a result of experiment here on Earth, but it must apply equally well everywhere else in the universe. So, armed with the known physical and mechanical principles, it becomes a question of mathematical analysis to settle the internal structure of the sun, and indeed of stars generally.

We can in the first place put the problem this way: Suppose we are given a definite quantity of material of known composition, then into what size body will it finally settle down, and how much radiant energy will it then give out at its surface? In other words, given the mass and composition of a star, what will be its radius and total luminosity? (Fig. 45.) This problem has in fact been solved theoretically, and as there are lots of stars for which the results are found to be in full accord with observation, including be it said some of the apparently most

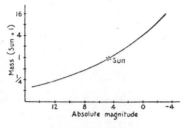

Fig. 45

Curve showing the relation between mass and brightness (absolute magnitude) of the stars. (The abs. mag. is the magnitude a star would have if seen at a standard distance of 32·63 light-years. The abs. mag. of the sun is 4·85, whereas its apparent magnitude is −26·72.) Five magnitudes corresponds to a *decrease* by $\frac{1}{100}$ in actual total energy output

exceptional kinds of stars, the theory must be regarded as satisfactory in all other respects, and accordingly the internal conditions can be decided from it. In stating the problem here we have regarded the mass and composition as known, and proceeded to the radius and luminosity, but in practice it is the latter two quantities that can be found for certain stars, and also in many cases the mass. It therefore becomes possible to reverse the procedure and discover from the theory the composition of such stars, and it is in this way that the prevailing conditions and internal constitution of the sun can be determined.

First, it has been found that as we go inwards from the solar surface, the temperature increases steadily all the way to the centre where it is about thirteen million degrees centigrade. The material itself is composed almost entirely of hydrogen (over ninety per cent) and helium, the two together comprising over ninety-eight per cent of the mass, with all the other elements amounting to less than two per cent, and distributed through the sun hardly more abundantly than sugar in a cake. At and near the centre the density is at least fifty times that of ordinary water, but nevertheless because of the high temperature the material behaves like an ordinary gas and is just as

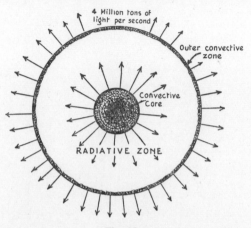

Fig. 46

A cross-section through the sun. The energy is generated in a central core at over 10 million degrees centigrade, where hydrogen is converted into helium. The energy released is carried outwards by both convection (turbulent motion of the material) and radiation, but outside the core it is carried almost entirely by radiation. Very near the surface convective motion of the material sets in again, though the main transfer of energy is still by radiation. At the outer surface 4 million tons of light escape freely every second to begin the long journey across space

compressible. It is the high pressure in these central regions that succeeds in compressing the hydrogen gas to this high density of more than fifty. The pressure at the centre of the sun is measured in hundreds of millions of atmospheres (Fig. 46).

In a central region extending out to about one-sixth the radius (that is about seventy thousand miles), the material is churning itself about with tremendous violence, called *convection*. It is as though the material were boiling strongly. This region, although having a volume of only one two-hundredth of the sun, nevertheless contains about a sixth of the total mass, and it is in this central *convective core*, as it is termed, that almost the whole of the sun's energy is generated. It does this, as already mentioned, by converting hydrogen into helium, a process that can take place spontaneously at temperatures of the order of ten million degrees or so. The process does not happen here on Earth, or anywhere else except in the stars, because the necessary temperatures by no means occur naturally. But if man can discover how to produce such temperatures and *control them* he may be able to rival the sun and obtain energy from hydrogen, of which the waters of the oceans contain a readily available abundance. If ever he can succeed in this, and the hydrogen bomb must be regarded as a big step towards the achievement, it will provide a source of energy that will far and away outmatch anything else hitherto attained, and supply all the needs of mankind on the most bountiful scale, other circumstances permitting, without fear of ever exhausting the supply. A few teaspoonfuls of water might provide enough energy to take a liner across the Atlantic and back, instead of the thousands of tons of oil needed at present. For the time being we have to be content to let the sun do the job for us, but he does so in a prodigiously wasteful roundabout way. Most of the light streams out into space nowhere near the Earth, which as we have seen in fact captures less than one two-thousand-millionth of the whole, and even of that reaching the Earth all but the minutest fraction fails to be converted to our eventual use.

Now although ten million degrees may seem, and is a pretty high temperature by any ordinary standards, it is now known that it is not nearly high enough for any elements other than helium to be built up from the hydrogen of which the sun and stars are initially formed. Hydrogen is to be regarded as constituting the primitive material of the universe from which all other elements are somehow formed. This conclusion has a highly important implication, because it means that in its present state neither the sun nor any similar star can produce the heavy elements that are essential for the formation of planets, such as our Earth, in which as we have seen it is the heavy elements that are abundant and the hydrogen by comparison exceedingly scarce. This difficulty had been recognised for many years by the physicists, who had early maintained that ordinary stars were not hot enough for the heavy elements to form. On the other hand Eddington, who was one of the great pioneers in the study of the interior of the stars, was so impressed by these theoretical temperatures of tens of millions of degrees when they first became recognised, that he felt sure they could not be bettered anywhere in the universe, and he was so confident that the physicists must be wrong that he publicly told them to "Go and find a hotter place"! The discovery of such a place or places has however had to be promoted from a mere jest to one of the most serious problems of astronomy, and it is now believed that such places do come to exist in certain stars from time to time for reasons that we shall describe in due course in the next chapter.

Returning now to the interior of the sun, in the region immediately outside the central convective core, the gaseous material is more or less stationary, and the outward flow of energy gradually traverses it mainly by the process of *radiation*, the process by which light-energy can cross space empty of matter. The energy is in this way handed on from particle to particle, the immense numbers of which blanket down and trap the energy as it slowly makes its way outwards. These particles alternately absorb and re-emit the energy, with only the most gradual leakage towards the surface of what in the interior is the tiniest proportion of all the energy on hand. Inside the sun there is ever present an enormous quantity of energy, already released and available in the form of radiation, that is only being prevented from flowing out into space by the material of the sun itself. There is enough free energy existing in the sun to keep it shining at its present rate for several million years even if the conversion of hydrogen should by some miracle cease, though not enough to keep it going for several *thousand* million years. The energy has to fight its way out through nearly half-a-million miles (the radius of the sun) of very opaque gases, which makes it easy to realise that there must always be a far greater quantity of energy on its way than the comparatively small amount that continually leaks out at the surface.

Finally, as we approach the surface layers from below, the

general violent boiling of the material, still mainly hydrogen, now sets in again and prevails to the surface. At slightly higher level still, the atmosphere begins to become increasingly transparent, and accordingly some of the light is able to escape freely and begin its long journey across space (Fig. 46).

Before concluding this chapter here is a thumbnail sketch of the sun giving the latest figures for its various properties:

Age: at least 5,000 million years.

Weight: 2×10^{27} tons (i.e. 2,000,000,000,000,000,000,000,000,000 tons).

Radius: 432,000 miles.

Average density: $1 \cdot 4$ times that of water (i.e. about a quarter the Earth's average density).

Composition: at least 90% hydrogen; more than 98% hydrogen and helium; less than 2% all other elements together.

Temperature: at outer surface 6000° centigrade, at the centre about 13,000,000° centigrade.

Light and energy output: 3×10^{27} candlepower, or 5×10^{23} horse-power.

It is perhaps desirable in concluding this chapter to emphasise again how very complex an astronomical engine the sun is, and how extremely difficult it proves to disentangle the light messages that are sent out, thereby to discover how the sun works. Although much is already known, especially about the major processes involved, far more remains to be discovered and understood about the details, and the problems they present are going to be unusually difficult to solve. Despite all the progress that has been made to date, there is no doubt whatever that the sun will long continue to live up to Shakespeare's description of him as "The heaven's glorious sun, that will not be deep-searched by saucy looks." But nevertheless astronomers are not to be put off by this warning, and are always doing their best to devise ever saucier ways of trying to penetrate his secrets. And as our very existence owes practically everything to him, this modern form of sun-worship is surely the least tribute that can be paid in return.

REFERENCES

The Birth and Death of the Sun, G. Gamow, Macmillan, 1941.
Eclipses of the Sun, S. A. Mitchell, New York, 1951.
Our Sun, D. H. Menzel, Harvard, 1949.
Eclipses of the Sun and Moon, F. W. Dyson and R. v. d. R. Woolley, Oxford, 1937.
Physics of the Sun and Stars, W. H. McCrea, Hutchinson, 1950.

V

THE STARS AND GALAXY

Isolation of Solar System—Other planetary systems impossible to detect—Number of stars—Size and shape of galaxy—Milky Way—Interstellar matter—Gas and Dust clouds—Formation of Comets—Ice ages—Other galaxies—Globular clusters—Magellanic clouds—Determination of distances—Parallax—Cepheid variables—Rotation of galaxy—Radial velocities—Doppler effect—Red-shift—Types of star—Double-stars—Red giants—White dwarfs—Composition of stars—Novae and Supernovae—Build-up of heavier elements—Crab nebula—Cause of supernovae—Origin of the planets, and of satellites and asteroids—Gradual change in orbits—Radio-astronomy.

THE ISOLATION OF OUR SOLAR SYSTEM

It is seldom realised how extraordinarily isolated in space our solar system is. We have seen that its own dimensions are very great by ordinary standards; light travelling at 186,000 miles per second takes more than five hours to come from its remotest visible components, Neptune and Pluto. But the light from the next nearest visible object beyond, which is the star Alpha Centauri, takes over four *years* to reach us here. In round numbers the distance is twenty-five million million miles. This means that the nearest known stars are more than eight thousand times as far away as the furthest of the planets. If an object as small as a golf ball were used to represent the sun, then on the same scale, Pluto would be a tiny speck two hundred yards away, but the nearest stars would be several hundred miles away. Because the distances are so great it is convenient to use the *light-year*, that is the distance light would travel in one year, as unit of distance, and this is equal to $5 \cdot 88 \times 10^{12}$ miles, that is about six billion miles. The brightest star in the heavens, Sirius, is about nine light-years away; it is not by any means intrinsically the brightest star, but we see it so mainly because of its proximity.

One simple consequence of these vast distances is that it is utterly impossible to discover whether any other star in the universe is attended by planets. Even a planet as large and bright as Jupiter would become quite invisible in the most powerful telescope if removed to the distance of the nearest stars, quite apart from the additional difficulty of the presence of a bright central star, playing the role of sun, only a few seconds of arc away and drowning out by its light every other object in the vicinity.

THE GALAXY

Now as we go on outwards through space the total number of stars is vast beyond conception. The whole galaxy, as the stellar system of which the sun is a single member is called, contains about one hundred thousand million, or 10^{11}, stars. The remotest of them are about eighty thousand light-years distant from the sun and ourselves. Our galaxy is a flat disc-shaped structure with a kind of bulge at the central part, rather like a fried-egg

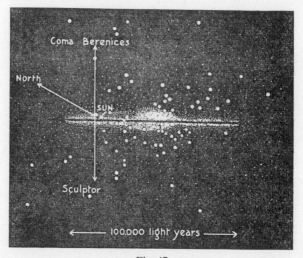

Fig. 47

Conjectural drawing of the galaxy as seen edge-on. The poles of the galactic plane are in the directions of the constellations of Coma Berenices and Sculptor. The sun is situated slightly above the central plane. The dark central band represents obscuration by galactic dust clouds. The small dots well outside the galaxy are a halo of widely-spaced surrounding stars. The large dots represent the globular clusters and show their distribution in relation to the galaxy

in shape with the yolk representing the bulge (Fig. 47). But the visible galaxy is formed of widely spaced stars, separated from each other by just such distances as separate the sun from its nearest stellar neighbours, with our sun itself situated about three-fifths of the way out from the centre and quite near the central plane. But this celestial fried-egg is a hundred thousand light-years across from one end of the diameter to the other, that is about six hundred thousand billion miles.

The galaxy has a general thickness, perpendicular to its plane, of about one-tenth its radius, which means a depth of

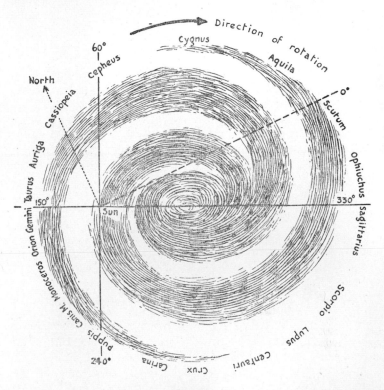

Fig. 48

Conjectural drawing of our galaxy in plan. The sun is believed to be near the edge of a spiral arm. The arms consist of stars and gas and dust clouds. The general plane of the galaxy is the plane of the Milky Way, the successive constellations of which are as indicated. (The north direction is 28° out of this plane.) As seen from the sun, the centre of the galaxy is in the direction of the constellation of Sagittarius, in galactic longitude 330°. The whole system is in rotation as indicated

about five thousand light-years at any rate at most parts. The stars we can see with our unaided eyes on a clear night are simply the visible ones of those in the immediate neighbourhood of the sun, and all these lie within a comparatively short distance of about a thousand light-years. As this is less than the extent of the galaxy perpendicular to its general plane, the stars within this distance appear to be spread out all round the sky. The total number of such stars visible to the unaided eye is about six or seven thousand, counting both hemispheres. But when we look along the plane of the galaxy we see not only the near stars, but a faint irregularly outlined band of light running in a broad belt right round the sky (Fig. 48). This faint haze of light is the cumulative effect of all the very much more distant stars, and it is this that constitutes the so-called Milky Way.

If we look out in directions perpendicular to the plane of the galaxy—the general plane defined by the Milky Way,—apart from the local bright ones, we see comparatively few stars, but if we look in directions along the plane there are immense numbers. Even a pair of ordinary field-glasses brings the total number of observable stars up to about 50,000, but a really big telescope can separate out some thousands of millions of them; even a small area of the Milky Way, say of the angular size of the moon, may show hundreds of thousands of stars.

INTERSTELLAR MATTER

But the stars constitute only a portion of the mass of the galaxy: exactly what proportion is not yet known, but almost certainly less than half the total mass. The space defined by the overall volume of the galaxy also contains clouds of highly rarefied material. The clouds are of two kinds, being made up of both solid dust particles and gas, the gaseous material consisting almost entirely of hydrogen. The dust, which often occurs in association with gas clouds, is a source of great trouble to astronomers, because it has tremendous powers of obscuration and can hide all the stars lying beyond. By weight, there is far less dust than hydrogen gas, perhaps only a fraction of one per cent is dust, but it is so finely divided that it can effectively obscure large regions of the galaxy; indeed, the most central regions of the galaxy in the direction of the constellation of Sagittarius are permanently hidden from observation by means of ordinary telescopes relying on visible and photographic light. These clouds tend to be quite separate affairs, possessing irregular shapes and ranging over many light-years in extent, though they differ greatly in size and form.

Just as do the stars, these clouds have their own motions within the galaxy, and it is possible that from time to time any star such as our sun may find itself passing slowly (that is, at a few miles a second) through a hydrogen or dust cloud. In either case the material will tend to be drawn into the star by

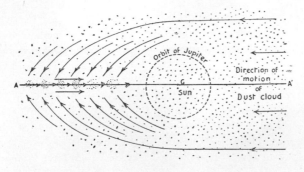

Fig. 49

The diagram represents a section through the accretion axis A′GA. The oncoming dust particles sweep round the sun and converge almost to this axis where they collide and collect together into much denser swarms that form the comets. These are attracted towards G, the centre of mass of the solar system, and so escape falling directly into the sun. (The cometary aggregates are much exaggerated in size in the diagram in order to show them at all, as also is the distance of G from the sun)

its gravitational attraction, and where hydrogen gas is concerned the star may be able to gather in large quantities to itself and substantially increase its mass, provided the density of the original cloud is high enough and the star moves sufficiently slowly through it. If the cloud consists of dust particles, the attraction of the star will deflect them inwards and focus them towards the axial line behind the star, and it can be shown that they will tend to gather into clumps of widely spaced particles, —though now far less widely spaced than in the original clouds (Fig. 49). This is probably how the comets form, and in the case of the sun the planets are there preventing the resulting comets from falling directly into it, by exerting small but sufficiently strong sideways forces on them. Passages of the sun through such clouds must have happened on many occasions in the course of the sun's long lifetime, and so there will have been numerous opportunities for the sun to replenish its stock of comets and thereby offset the steady dissipation of them that we have seen goes on.

In the case of gaseous material, we have already seen how the general infall into the sun may be connected with the existence of the corona, and this suggests that the sun may even at the present time be moving through an extremely tenuous cloud (the density of material would need to be of order 10^{-24} grams per cubic centimetre i.e. one billion-billionth, but the precise value also depends on the speed of the sun moving through it). If in the past the density of the cloud were higher, or the velocity slower, or even both, the amount of infalling material could become very much greater, and this in turn could affect the total emission of energy at the sun's surface. A change in the sun's luminosity by only a few percent might have very serious influence on the Earth's climate, and accordingly it has been suggested that many of the former great vicissitudes in terrestrial climate, namely the ice-ages, may have been caused by such changes in the sun's emission. Curiously enough it had long since been maintained by many climatologists that what is needed to produce an ice-age is an *increase* in the sun's total heat output, and not a decrease as one might expect, owing to the indirect effect of the resulting clouds reflecting light and heat back into space, and this is exactly what an astronomical cause of the present kind could produce.

OTHER GALAXIES

It used to be thought not so very long ago (less than half a century) that this galaxy of ours comprised the whole material universe. But certain small faint patches of nebulous light, other than those due to the actual galactic gas-clouds already mentioned, are now known to be gigantic island-universes similar in size and shape to our own galaxy, but lying far outside it. Hundreds of millions of these so-called extra-galactic nebulae are now known to exist, completely separated from our galaxy and each containing thousands of millions of stars. Several of the nearer examples of these objects enable a very clear idea to be obtained of what our own galaxy is probably like, for from our distant vantage point we can view these external objects in their entirety, whereas we are so deeply immersed inside our own vast galaxy, with its obscuring dust clouds, that it is far more difficult for that very reason to ascertain its precise form.

Some of these external systems happen to lie edge on to us and show what our galaxy would look like seen from far out in its own general plane. These edge-on nebulae usually show a dark band along their central plane resulting from the cumulative effect of all the dark dust clouds in them. The presence of much the same belt of dust clouds in our own galaxy manifests itself quite clearly by the fact that external objects are only to be found at fairly high angular directions away from the general galactic plane. It cannot be supposed that there are any real preferential directions for independent outside objects, and the effect, known as the zone of avoidance, is due simply to obscuration by our own galactic dust (Fig. 50).

Other galaxies are more or less flat on to us, and many of them although roughly circular and disc-shaped show overall spiral formations, with the result that these external galaxies are often called spiral nebulae, though they by no means all show these spiral arms. There is, by good fortune, what is now believed to be almost a twin of our own galaxy quite near to us in the direction of the constellation of Andromeda, though of course it lies far beyond any of the stars of our own galaxy that go to make up this constellation. "Quite near" in this connection actually means a million and a half (1,500,000) light-years! The bright central part of this particular nebula can be faintly seen, as about a fourth magnitude object, with the unaided eye. Incidentally it is the remotest object in the universe visible without optical aid. Its general plane is not quite edge-on but somewhat inclined, so that we see it obliquely. The arms are composed not only of stars but of clouds of gas and dust. The separate gas-clouds are too small in comparison with the whole to be seen individually, and accordingly they give the appearance when the nebula is viewed as a whole of more or less continuous streamers.

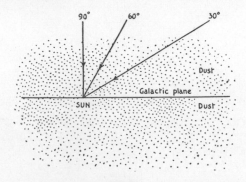

Fig. 50

Zone of avoidance caused by galactic dust. The longer the path through interstellar dust the more obscuration occurs. It is least for objects in the directions of the galactic poles ($\pm 90°$), and increases as the direction approaches the plane of the galaxy. Only few globular clusters or extragalactic nebulae are found within $\pm 20°$ of this plane, and almost none at all within $\pm 5°$

THE GLOBULAR CLUSTERS

Surrounding our own galaxy, in a kind of spherical halo, and not showing any special association with the general galactic plane, is a much more diffuse distribution of stars, and also a considerable number of the mysterious objects called globular clusters (Fig. 47). About a hundred of these latter are known, and each one is a self-contained cluster of something like a hundred thousand individual stars kept together by their own mutual gravitation. The stars become more and more widely spaced the further out they are in the cluster. In a photograph of one of these objects, the stars near the centre, where we are looking through the greatest depth of the cluster anyway, run together on the plate and do not show as separate stars, but actually vast distances separate adjacent stars—distances of the order of fifty thousand times the Earth's distance from the sun. The dense central portion of such a cluster is about twenty light-years across, but the whole extent out to the faintest visible stars is fully one hundred light-years. The nearest and brightest of these to our part of the galaxy is omega-Centauri, to be seen only from more southerly latitudes than ours, which globular cluster is about 20,000 light-years away and looks like a faint hazy star of the fourth magnitude. The brightest visible example (telescopically only) in the northern hemisphere is termed Messier 13 (its original number in Messier's catalogue), and is at a distance of 35,000 light-years. Most of them are two or three times as far away as this, but the most distant so far discovered (N.G.C. 7006) is 230,000 light-years away. The light by which we see even the nearest of them has been travelling on its way (at 186,000 miles a second) for longer than civilisation (as we know it) has existed, while for the remotest of them probably longer than the human species has existed. Yet they are still part and parcel of our own local galactic system undoubtedly connected with it gravitationally.

At one time the distribution of the globular clusters in the heavens was regarded as very mysterious and peculiar, for they were found to lie almost entirely in one half of the sky, as we see them. But the reason is now known to be simple enough, and it is merely because the sun is fairly well out towards the edge of the galaxy, whereas the globular clusters are symmetrically distributed round its centre. The whole group of globular clusters are spread out through a spherical volume very slightly flattened to the galactic plane, and some two hundred thousand light-years across. The median plane of the distribution coincides with the general plane of the galaxy, and the sun is considerably removed from the centre of the distribution, which coincides with the centre of the galaxy. There are no globular clusters to be seen within about six thousand light-years of the plane of the Milky way, but the reason for this is likely to be, not that none exists, but that any that do lie there are hidden from view by obscuring dust, as already explained.

THE MAGELLANIC CLOUDS

Also, further still outside our galaxy and separated from it, but still bound to it by gravitational forces, are two huge irregular clouds each containing millions of stars. These are the famous Magellanic Clouds, named after the Portuguese navigator Magellan, and they are plainly visible to the naked eye but only far south in the sky removed from northern latitudes. Their contents, in the way of types of stars and gaseous nebulae, suggest that they are detached portions of our own galaxy, and there are even a few globular clusters associated with the Large Cloud. The distance of this one is about two hundred thousand light-years, while the Small Cloud is about fifteen thousand light-years nearer. They themselves are separated by about eighty-thousand light-years. The Large Cloud is about thirty-thousand light-years across, and the smaller cloud about half that distance in extent.

DETERMINATION OF STELLAR DISTANCES

The way in which the distances of the nearer stars are found is simple enough in principle, depending on an application of the same triangulation process from a known base-line that has already been explained in connection with the determination of the distance of the moon, and that of the sun. But when it comes to the stars, any base-line that we can take on Earth (the maximum is eight thousand miles) is hopelessly inadequate for measuring a distance of at least twenty-five million million miles, which is that of even the nearest known star. What is done in practice is to take advantage of the movement of the Earth from one side of the sun to the other. Thus at intervals six-months apart we are transported bodily from one side of the sun to the other by 186,000,000 miles—twice the sun's distance —and although this gives a much more sizeable base-line, it is still only passably useful, serving only for near stars within about a thousand light-years.

Because of the Earth's motion round the sun, the very nearest of the stars appear to rock to and fro in the sky as compared with the much more distant background ones, which appear absolutely fixed. This motion is called the *parallax* effect, and it exactly reflects in miniature the Earth's motion round the sun (Fig. 51). The amount by which even the closest stars oscillate in the sky through this cause is a very small angle, less than one thousandth of the (angular) width of the moon, and actually about one and a half seconds of arc (there are 3600 seconds of arc in one degree). Once this angular displacement has been measured, the distance of the star follows from the known size of the Earth's path round the sun. This is one of the reasons why astronomers take such pains to find out the distance of the sun with the highest accuracy, though many other things in astronomy are also intimately related to the so-called solar parallax.

Now although this method is satisfactory only for the few thousand stars in our immediate neighbourhood (by galactic standards), which are a negligible proportion of the whole, this

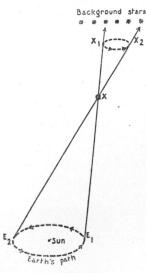

Fig. 51

Parallax effect of the Earth's annual motion round the sun. When the Earth is at E_1 a near star X will be seen in the direction X_1 relative to much more distant background stars. Six months later the Earth is at E_2 and the star will be seen in direction X_2. This angular displacement is termed *parallax*, and the angle E_2XE_1 depends on the star's distance. (The diagram is nothing like to scale: the greatest known value of the angle E_2XE_1 is about $1''.5$ for the star α Centauri)

survey nevertheless covers a sufficiently wide sample of types of stars for a fairly clear conception of the general characteristics of all the stars to be obtained. It is rather as though, say, five-thousand people were selected more or less at random from all over the world; a study of these would give fairly reliable evidence about people as a whole even though there may be thousands of millions of them. In this way it has been found that certain types of stars, distinguishable and classifiable by means of the spectroscope without regard to their distance, are pretty well all of the same intrinsic brightness wherever they happen to occur. The apparent differences of brightness of the members of such a class are due simply to their differing distances. Obviously the further away a star is the fainter it will be; if it were twice as far away it would be only one-quarter as bright; three times as far away and it would be one-ninth as bright, and so on. But if it is known by other means how intrinsically bright a star really is, then its apparent brightness will obviously enable its true distance to be found.

THE CEPHEID VARIABLES

But in addition to these stars that can be classified by means of the spectroscope, Nature has been particularly helpful in providing a distribution through the galaxy of certain extremely bright stars, called Cepheid variables, that enable distances to be measured for which the ordinary parallax method would be hopelessly ineffective. Moreover their great brightness enables them to be detected at correspondingly great distances. Cepheids (pronounced See-fee-ids) are very readily identified, because the total light of any such star varies in an absolutely characteristic way that can soon be recognised. What happens is that the star undergoes a rapid increase in brightness followed by a comparatively much slower decrease, then it brightens up again in exactly the same way and slowly fades back again, the whole change being continuously and regularly repeated with perfectly definite period (Fig. 52). This class of stars takes its name from the particular star delta-Cephei, which is a standard example of them all. For this particular variable, the total light output rather more than doubles in about twenty-four hours, and then in the next four days it gradually decreases back to the original value; then it quickly brightens again and slowly fades in exactly the same way. Always a rapid rise followed by slow fall. For this star the whole rhythmical cycle of change is gone through in about five and a third days, and the period is perfectly regular from one cycle to the next.

But different Cepheids have different light changes, some brighten up as much as sixfold, and different periods, some

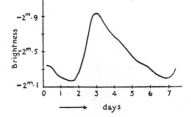

Fig. 52

The light curve of delta-Cephei. The rapid rise to maximum followed by a slower fall is characteristic of Cepheid variables. The total light just about doubles. The period is about 5⅓ days

taking less than a day to go through the changes and some taking as long as a fortnight. And it is here that their crucial distance-revealing property enters: the longer the period, the brighter the star, and in a perfectly definite relation. If the intrinsic or absolute brightnesses of several Cepheid variables are

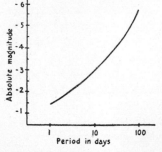

Fig. 53

The Period-Luminosity law for Cepheids. If the period is known, the absolute magnitude of the star can be read off the curve and compared with the apparent magnitude to give the distance. (Abs. mag. is the brightness at a specified distance 32·6 light years, and −5 magnitudes correspond to a factor of 100 in actual brightness)

plotted one by one against their periods, the points obtained lie on a simple curve (Fig. 53). And then by making use of the curve, if the period is known, the brightness can be read off. Now the period of a star whose light is varying regularly is one of the easiest things to measure; all that is necessary is to observe the star for a sufficient time, or record its light photo-electrically. The discovery of likely Cepheids in the first place is also much facilitated because they tend to lie very close to the central plane of the galaxy—the galactic plane—and are highly luminous stars, several thousand times as bright as the sun in many cases.

The discovery of this property of the Cepheid-variables was first made from a study of the stars contained in the Magellanic Clouds. The lesser of these contains something like half a million stars, and hundreds of them show the characteristic light-variation of Cepheids. Also the cloud, lying right outside our own galaxy as it does, is sufficiently compact for all the stars in it to be regarded as being at practically the same distance from the observer, even though they are somewhat scattered over a considerable volume locally. In this way the distance effect is eliminated, except in so far as it reduces the brightness of all the stars equally, and the relative brightnesses of the stars as they are seen in the cloud are practically the same as their relative real intrinsic brightnesses. For example, if one star of the cloud *looks* twice as bright as another in total light, then it will be intrinsically twice as bright, and would appear so from whatever (equal) distance the two stars are observed. It was in this way that the general form of the so-called Period-Luminosity curve was first found.

This achieved, it only remains to find by other means the actual distances of a few of the nearer Cepheids in our own galaxy, in order to determine the actual or absolute brightnesses of a few Cepheids of known periods, and this then anchors the whole curve once and for all. Then having got the curve, all that has to be done is to watch any Cepheid variable long enough to get its period, read off its absolute luminosity from the curve, compare this with how bright it seems to be, and the distance then follows. The application of this simple empirical rule has played a tremendously important role in fixing the general dimensions of our own galaxy, and indeed in determining the scale of the whole universe, as will be seen in due course.

It is in this way then that the general size and shape of our own galaxy has been found; that it is a flattened disc-shaped structure some hundred thousand light-years in diameter, with the sun quite close to its general plane and about thirty thousand light years from the centre. But although this is one of the chief ways of surveying the galaxy, there are other ways too of obtaining the results, and testing them to see if everything is indeed consistent. This work has been steadily and successfully carried on within the last half-century, and the dimensions and form of the galaxy are now established beyond any possibility of serious revision being required. Much remains to be filled in as to details, such as the exact position and form of the spiral arms, while other regions unfortunately are permanently obscured from us by dust clouds. The main difficulty here is that we are inside the galaxy and this makes it hard to see the wood for the trees. In the case of other galaxies external to ours the general features can be taken in at a glance.

THE ROTATION OF THE GALAXY

Now it is evident that the galaxy must involve some feature that prevents it from collapsing under its own self-attraction, and it has been discovered that this is achieved by the whole vast assembly being in rotation; this is what gives the galaxy its flat circular disc-like shape—a huge celestial catherine wheel. Each individual star and gas-cloud in the system is describing a more or less circular path round the centre of the galaxy, and it is the outward centrifugal force due to this motion that balances the inward gravitational attraction of all the material, stars, gas, and dust, of the galaxy. The mechanism is similar to that in the solar system where the motion of the planets prevents them from falling directly into the sun, except that in the galaxy the mass is no longer concentrated entirely in a single body but to a considerable extent spaced through the whole system. In the galaxy, as for the planetary system, the inner parts go round in less time than the outer parts, so that the system is not rotating as if it were a solid disc.

At the sun's position the time for one revolution round the galaxy is about two hundred million years. The solar system with everything in it, ourselves included, is undergoing this motion. But so vast is the galaxy, the sun has to travel at nearly two hundred miles per second to complete the circle even in this great time interval. Not only the sun, but all the near stars that we see at night have much the same speed in the galaxy; the slight differences give rise to much smaller relative velocities between local stars. In the whole lifetime of the sun it has made only about twenty-five to thirty circuits of the galaxy. Nearer the central regions the time an individual star takes for a round trip is considerably less, something like one hundred million years, whilst further out beyond the sun the time for a complete revolution exceeds two hundred million years by increasing amounts.

RADIAL VELOCITIES OF STARS

If the galaxy were rotating like a solid wheel, the distance between any two of its parts would remain unchanged, and it would scarcely be possible to detect the rotation by any observations made within the system. But actually different parts are moving at different angular speeds, and the distances between stars at different distances from the centre are always undergoing change.

Now it turns out that any motion of a star either directly towards or away from us—motion in the line of sight, as it is called—can be measured immediately by means of the spectroscope. The principle is simple enough. Everyone will have noticed how the horn of an approaching motor-car literally shrieks until the car is alongside, and then suddenly the note drops right down to a deep bass as soon as the car begins to recede. It is a question of the number of waves of sound per second reaching us, for this is what determines the note we hear. When the car is approaching, successive waves are close together, and the note is raised; when it is receding they are further apart, and the note is then lowered. The effect is easily noticeable because the speeds of motor-cars, though much smaller, are nevertheless a moderate fraction of the speed of sound (760 miles per hour). Now the relative motions of the stars involve speeds of many miles per second, in this case a small but appreciable part of the speed of light (186,000 miles per second), and these affect the light we receive from them in much the same way. It is called the Doppler effect in both cases, for sound and for light.

If the light-source is approaching, the wave-lengths become shorter, and light tends to become bluer or more violet, whereas if it is receding the light becomes reddened. But in order to measure the amount by which this happens, and so find the speed, the light must first be split up into its individual colours and lines, corresponding to the notes of sound, and it is this that the spectroscope can do.

It has already been explained how if sunlight is passed through a narrow slit before being sent through a glass prism the continuous beam of light so formed is crossed by a number of distinct dark lines. If the source of light is at rest, these lines come in absolutely fixed positions. But if the source is moving towards the apparatus, these lines are displaced towards the violet end of the spectrum by amounts depending directly on the speed. In any given line, if the speed is doubled, its displacement from its standard position is doubled. But the displacement also depends on the original wave-length, so that all lines are not shifted the same amount, the longer wave-lengths (at the red end of the spectrum) are shifted more than the shorter ones (at the violet end). Similarly if the source of light is receding, the displacement of all lines is towards the red end of the spectrum by amounts depending on the speed and on the wave-length. For large displacements due to recession this is often called "red-shift."

So if the light of a star is passed through a spectroscope, and particular lines are selected, such as those giving a recognisable pattern, their displacements from their standard positions immediately reveal how fast the star is moving towards or away from us. The kind of speeds involved for various stars average anything up to twenty or thirty miles per second, though a small proportion are much higher and some much lower. The measurement reveals only that part of the motion that is taking the star directly away or towards us, any motion sideways or transversely has no effect on the light. For this reason the speeds measured with the spectroscope are called *radial velocities*, because they refer only to motion along the radius from the observer to the star. They can be found practically instantaneously for any given star, without having to wait many years to see the effect of the motion, as unfortunately is necessary for the sideways components of their motions, usually termed the *proper motions*. Moreover radial velocities can not only be measured much more readily, but more accurately than transverse motions, and all this goes to make radial speeds very important. Once these speeds are known for a sufficient number of stars, the overall picture of the general rotation of the galaxy can be arrived at.

SPECIAL TYPES OF STAR

For some types of star the measured radial velocities show regular changes. For example, in the case of the Cepheids, it is found that as the light changes so the size of the star changes, the surface that emits the light alternately rising and falling rhythmically. The speeds up and down are of the order of a few miles per second, and the spectroscope easily reveals them superposed on the displacements of lines due to the general motion of the star as a whole towards or away. These stars must actually be pulsating in some way and changing their size regularly, but the causes are still far from being understood. It has been held that the oscillations are due to a slightly unstable energy output deep down inside that keeps the pulsations going like a heat-engine. But the motion is so perfectly regular that gravitational forces seem more likely to be involved, and for this reason as well as others it has been suggested that a Cepheid may consist of two stars but surrounded by a common screening atmosphere which pulsates up and down, without rotation, as the two hidden stars revolve round each other deep down below the surface.

There are in fact lots of double-stars in the galaxy in which the two component stars are quite separate and distinct bodies.

In the so-called *visual* double-stars, the telescope can actually separate the two and make both visible. There are also triple, and quadruple star systems, and indeed systems of far greater complexity still gravitationally bound together as complex clusters of stars in motion about each other. In many double-systems, however, the two stars are too close even for the most powerful telescope to separate them, but the presence of the two is revealed by the spectroscope which shows two separate sets of spectral lines, one corresponding to each component, and these move relative to each other in the spectrum in a perfectly rhythmical way corresponding exactly to the motion of the stars round each other. Such stars are called *spectroscopic binaries*, but they form only a small proportion of all the binary stars in the heavens. Something like 50% of all the stars have one or more companion stars moving round them. At one end of the scale the component stars are almost in contact and revolve about each other in a matter of hours or days, while at the other end the separations are thousands of times the Earth's distance from the sun and the periods tens or even hundreds of thousands of years.

THE RED GIANTS

The individual stars that go to make up binaries and multiple systems are themselves usually in other respects quite normal stars. By a normal star is meant one whose luminosity and radius both have standard ordinary values. To take the luminosity first, the brightness of a star depends almost entirely on its mass and on very little else, largely because stars consist principally of hydrogen and so have much the same compositions. The total luminosity of a star depends roughly on the cube of its mass, so that a star twice the mass of the sun would be intrinsically about eight times as bright; a star ten times as massive as the sun would be about a thousand times the sun's brightness, and so on. The radius of a star, however, although increasing directly with the mass, does not do so quite as fast but roughly only as the two-thirds power. This means that a star twice as massive as the sun will have rather less than twice the sun's radius, in fact about 1·6 solar radii. A star eight times the sun's mass will normally have radius about four times that of the sun.

There are, however, certain stars called "red giants" that fail to satisfy this second rule, though conforming all right to the first where their total luminosity is concerned. These stars are much more massive than the sun, at least ten times so, and accordingly, quite apart from any question of their radius, have had time to reduce their hydrogen-contents very considerably. If such a star is able to gather in additional hydrogen at its surface, as for instance while passing through a hydrogen gas-cloud, the resulting difference of composition as between its inner and outer parts can bring about an enormous increase of radius—tenfold or far larger increases are easily possible—precisely because of the lightness of hydrogen compared with the material of the interior, but the change in size scarcely affects the deep interior at all, and the amount of energy driven out from the central regions is unaltered. This means that the luminosity itself is unchanged, but because of the increased size the outer surface area is also greatly increased, and the star now necessarily gives out less light through a given area of its surface than it would otherwise do. It achieves this by being cooler at the surface, which means that it appears redder. A star that normally might have a surface-temperature of more than 10,000 degrees, when it becomes a red giant may have a surface-temperature of less than 3000 degrees, the exact value depending on the precise extension of the radius.

Many examples of such stars have been found, perhaps the best known being the bright red star Betelgeuse (pronounced beetle-jooze) in the constellation of Orion. This has a mass about fifteen times that of the sun, but its radius instead of being merely ten times that of the sun averages about 250 solar radii. If the sun were transported to its centre, the whole of the Earth's orbit would easily fit inside it. Normally a star of this mass would have outer surface temperature approaching about 20,000 degrees, but Betelgeuse actually exhibits one of only about 3,000 degrees, and it is this that makes it look so very red compared with other stars. It is in fact also variable in size, the radius ranging irregularly from just over two hundred solar radii to nearly three hundred. The general order of the time taken for the changes is about six years but there is no definite period of oscillation, as there is for a Cepheid for example.

Another similar example is provided by the red star Antares. It is about twice as massive as Betelgeuse and its radius is over 450 times that of the sun, so that if it were imagined placed at the sun the orbits of all the inner planets, Mars included, would lie inside it. The possibility that the sun itself, after suitably increasing its mass from interstellar hydrogen, might at some future period swell out to become a red giant and thereby gradually swallow the inner planets, has been held out as one of the ways in which the solar system might cease to exist as such. But the increased brightness, probably by many hundred times, of the sun that would precede the red giant stage would in any case probably have already terminated mankind's interest in the future of the planetary system.

Large as these two stars Betelgeuse and Antares are, fairly recent examples have been discovered of far larger red giants still. One component of the star epsilon-Aurigae has a radius about two thousand times that of the sun which would mean it could contain the whole orbit of Saturn inside it; while according to some estimates one component of the double-system *VV* Cephei has truly gigantic size, being three thousand times that of the sun in radius.

All these stars have incredibly low densities, even taking the average, in most cases less than one millionth part of our ordinary air at ground level, which is about 0.0013 grams per cubic centimetre. (One litre of our ordinary air weighs about 1·3 grams, or rather less than $\frac{1}{20}$th of an ounce.) But the density in the outer parts of these stars must be a million times less still, and probably far lower than any "vacuum" that can be produced here on Earth.

THE WHITE DWARFS

At right the other end of the scale is another very curious class of stars, the white dwarfs, which as their name implies are extremely small. These are the remnants of stars that have exhausted almost all their available hydrogen, and are collapsed down to extraordinarily high densities. The amount of light they give out is far below standard for ordinary stars of comparable mass, yet because they are so small their tiny surfaces have to be quite bright to get rid even of the little light they emit; hence they have fairly high surface temperatures and appear "white." The most famous example is a companion star to Sirius, itself the brightest star in the sky. It turns out to have just less than the sun's mass, but is only about one three-hundredth as bright. In size it is not very much larger than the Earth, and this means that its average density is something like 50,000 times that of water. A cubic foot of its material would weigh over a thousand tons. Another even more extreme example is provided by van Maanen's star, for which the mean density is about ten times as great as that of Sirius B.

There is reason to suppose that white dwarfs may be very numerous; their extreme faintness makes them difficult to detect except in the immediate neighbourhood of the sun, but nevertheless many have been found. As will be explained later, they probably represent the final stage to which originally much more massive stars are reduced, as a result of their evolution, when they no longer keep up their internal energy generation, and with it the high internal temperature and pressure needed to withstand the tendency to collapse that any large mass must have under its own gravitational attraction.

THE COMPOSITION OF THE STARS

Perhaps the greatest of all triumphs of the spectroscope is that by its means even the compositions of the stars, or at any rate their visible outer layers, can be found. A century or so ago, this question of the composition of the stars was selected by the philosopher Comte as an example of one that must forever remain unanswerable. But unheeding science comprehends little of the highsounding claims of the pure philosophers, and has taken the problem in its stride. The identification of the elements existing there, and the determination of the prevailing conditions in the outer parts of the stars, from which the light is finally dispatched, is commonplace routine in observatories, and nowadays there is really little need for Joxer Daly to go on asking "What is the Stars?".

The practical reasons involved are simple enough. If any particular vaporised element, such as iron say, is set to shine and radiate light by suitably heating it, the light it gives out has a characteristic set of lines associated with it in the resulting spectrum, and every individual one of them always comes in exactly the same position. The precise positions of these in the spectrum, and the intensities of light in them can also be measured with high accuracy. Other elements and substances (compounds of elements) each have their own set of characteristic lines coming in quite different positions, and these have strengths depending on the conditions. The experienced spectroscopist can recognise the lines of a particular substance even though only a few may be visible, just as a musician might recognise a complicated piece of music even though he hears the merest snatch of melody from it. Experience and practice, in this as in other matters, bring almost unbelievable skill, and complicated as stellar spectra seem at first sight, in the hands of experts they nevertheless yield up the compositions of the stars' atmospheres with absolute certainty.

To take the sun, for example, its spectrum shows that hydrogen is enormously abundant, constituting over ninety per cent of the substance of its outer layers. Helium is next in abundance with perhaps a few per cent—this gas by the way was discovered in the sun spectroscopically before it was actually found and identified on Earth, and hence its name (*helios* is a Greek word for the sun)—while all the other elements together, iron, calcium, sodium, nickel, cobalt, copper, zinc, to mention only just a few of the metals found in the sun, total up only about one or two per cent of the whole mass. Although a particular substance may be present only to a very minute extent, if conditions of temperature and pressure are favourable, it can nevertheless cause conspicuously strong lines. Calcium, for instance, produces two very strong dark lines fairly close together at the violet end of the spectrum, showing that calcium is present absorbing the light that would otherwise be given out at those wavelengths, and these same lines also appear in the spectra of many other stars. These particular lines, usually referred to as the H and K lines of calcium, are readily identifiable, and for this reason have come to play a specially important role in the measurement of the radial velocities of the most remote objects in the universe, namely the galaxies of stars external to our own stellar system.

NOVAE AND SUPERNOVAE

From an astronomical standpoint, as has already been mentioned in considering the composition of the Earth, the elements other than hydrogen and helium are usually all grouped together as the so-called heavy elements, while hydrogen and helium constitute the light elements. Thus the situation in both the outer and inner parts of the sun is very much the same as regards composition, and the complete reverse of the situation for the Earth. The Earth's composition, as we have seen, is almost entirely heavy elements; oxygen, silicon, aluminium, iron, calcium, and such like make up ninety-eight% of the total, while hydrogen contributes less than one%. But almost everywhere we turn amongst the stars, exactly the opposite holds, and hydrogen is in tremendous abundance. The same is also true of interstellar matter. But although it is almost all hydrogen, the cosmical dust clouds cannot be entirely hydrogen and helium, because these are gases, whereas the dust is small solid particles and must largely consist of heavy elements. The question therefore arises as to where this cosmic dust comes from, and accordingly we find the problem of the origin of the heavy elements turns up again from another direction.

It must be explained at this stage that within the past decade or so it has become practically certain that hydrogen provides the fundamental primitive building material in the universe from which all other elements are somehow formed. Fifty years ago, when the radioactive properties of various heavy elements, such as uranium, were first come upon, it was thought that possibly here at last was the source of the great energies of the stars. Theories of the structure of the stars were accordingly soon developed that pictured them as formed of ultra-heavy elements—far heavier than any actually known to exist on Earth—that gradually broke down into lighter elements, with the lightest element hydrogen the very last product of all. Influenced by such ideas, even as recently as twenty years ago, many astronomers found it hard to believe that there could be more than a few per cent of hydrogen in the stars, and all the then current theories of stellar structure and evolution were in great difficulties as a result. But the matter is much clearer today; the cookery of the elements is nowadays actually taking place (on a small scale) in laboratories as a regular thing, and is no longer a speculative process. This is how it has become certain that hydrogen is to be regarded as the prime element from which all the others must be built up.

But it has been seen that in any ordinary star like the sun the temperature is high enough for helium alone to be produced. Only if we can find places where the temperature is far greater will it be possible for heavy elements to form. For a long time this was a most perplexing problem, but it now looks pretty safe to say that the places where this can happen are in the central regions of certain stars called *supernovae*. So it is necessary to explain next what a supernova is.

It is found that certain stars suddenly blaze out quite unexpectedly with great violence, the total brightness increasing perhaps in a matter of hours by an enormous factor, and then gradually dying away again, taking many months or even years to do so. Every year on the average about a score of stars within our own galaxy undergo this catastrophic development and become what are termed *novae*. At their brightest they become anything up to a hundred-thousand times as luminous as the sun. Such exploding stars, however, are only ordinary novae, but in addition to these, and far more rarely, occur super-explosions in which the brightness may suddenly increase to about a thousand-million times the sun's brightness. Within our own galaxy such *supernovae* occur only once every two or three centuries on the average, but they are to be observed far more frequently in other external galaxies simply because there are so many of these objects for supernovae to happen in. A single star has sometimes flared up to become brighter for a few days than all the other thousands of millions of stars in the galaxy concerned put together. There is no doubt of this because it is a direct observational fact.

During this tremendous increase in brightness the star actually throws off material into the surrounding space, and has the appearance of ejecting expanding shells of matter. The whole star has quite evidently undergone an internal explosion of unsurpassable violence. To the continued disappointment of astronomers no instance has occurred within our own Milky Way system since the invention of the telescope, but one might occur at any time. The last recorded instance was in 1604 when a star, hitherto quite unobservable, suddenly appeared, and remained brighter than Jupiter for several weeks; after that it was distinctly visible to the unaided eye for nearly two years, before finally disappearing again. Not long before was the famous nova of 1572, which for some days was brighter than Venus, then gradually waned off before finally becoming invisible after about a year and a half. It may be any one of several faint stars that can now be detected near the recorded place. Yet another supernova within our galaxy was the nova of the year A.D. 1054, seen and carefully recorded by the Chinese. In the position of this explosion is now to be seen a vast nebula thirty million million miles across, known as the Crab nebula. It has taken nine hundred years for the gas to spread out this far.

THE CAUSE OF SUPERNOVAE

As has already been explained, if we have a star, say ten times as massive as the sun, it will be sending out light and energy at about a *thousand* times the total rate that the sun does, and so mass for mass it will be using up its hydrogen a *hundred* times as fast as the sun is doing. Now in its whole lifetime the sun has used up only a few per cent of its hydrogen, and if we put it at as little as five per cent, say, then other things being equal the more massive star would have got through the whole of its supply in only about one-fifth the time. So any such star beginning its career simultaneously with the sun, but ten times as massive, would long since have exhausted all its hydrogen, if this were not otherwise replenished. Now when a star no longer has hydrogen to burn, in order to keep up its energy output it begins to shrink and collapse, thereby raising its internal temperature to still higher values. When a sufficiently high central temperature is reached certain of the heavier elements can begin to be formed. But the processes involved now mainly absorb heat from the interior regions instead of providing it, and although rising to thousands of millions of degrees the temperature needed to produce pressure sufficient to stabilise the star is not forthcoming, and when this stage is reached the star collapses even more violently in a matter of mere minutes.

But any self-contained system such as a star, if it possesses rotational momentum, as stars must be supposed to do in different degrees, cannot get rid of this by any possible internal means. Accordingly the more the star shrinks the faster will it rotate, and this will continue until the rotational speeds are so great at the outer parts that owing to centrifugal force material begins to be flung off from the surface, incidentally thereby exposing the far hotter interior. It is this that sends up the brightness temporarily by such extraordinary amounts, for it must be remembered that brightness depends on the fourth power of the temperature, so that a hundredfold increase in temperature of exposed surface means a brightness increase, area for area, by about one hundred million. Also it is possible for a star undergoing a catastrophe of this order to shower out into space the greater part of its mass, now transformed to heavy elements, and retain the remainder in the form of a compact nucleus of extraordinarily high density, a white dwarf. It is in processes of this sort that the material to form the great irregular tracts of interstellar dust has probably been originated. The heavy elements are scattered out of stars that reach this supernova stage, and then after cooling down collect together into the tiniest grains of solid particles, to make themselves known to us by their great power of obscuration.

THE ORIGIN OF THE PLANETS

Now suppose a supernova explosion of this kind happened to a star, much more massive than the sun, that was a companion to the sun five thousand million years ago, and moved round the sun at a distance somewhere in the neighbourhood of Jupiter and Saturn's present distances. Lots of such widely separated double-stars are known to exist, so there is nothing untoward about such a hypothesis. Now the violence of the explosion would be so great that the slightest asymmetry in it would produce a recoil on the remaining nucleus of the exploding star that would easily pull it away from the sun altogether. An increase in speed of about ten miles per second would suffice for this, but the speeds at which material is showered off run up to thousands of miles a second, and several times the mass of the sun would have been ejected. So there is no difficulty in supposing that the explosion could result in the escape of the remaining stellar nucleus from the sun's attraction. Also, most of the material ejected in the explosion would easily escape from the sun because of its high speed, but the speeds would be distributed in all directions; and only one per cent of all the material ejected would weigh something like fifty times all the present planets put together. So it is only necessary to suppose that a small fraction of one per cent remained behind captured by the sun, a mere puff of smoke from the whole vast inferno, and this would provide enough to make all the planets. Also, because of the same supernova process, it would be composed principally of heavy elements.

This material would initially be at very high temperature, and therefore gaseous in form, and it cannot be supposed that it would immediately condense into planets. What it would do is to spread out into a huge flat disc of material surrounding the sun, rather like a gigantic Saturnian ring, but necessarily much further out from the central body (the sun) in comparison. This ring would cool into separate small solid particles, and these would begin to collect together gradually. It can be shown that small aggregates of varying sizes would form to begin with, but that once formed the largest of them would continue to grow much faster, swallowing up some of the smaller concerns too, after the manner of financial corporations under laisser-faire.

Accordingly what would result to begin with would be that a few large planets would form moving round the sun at distances comparable with those of the great outer planets at the present time. But as such bodies pulled in more and more material from the disc, they must inevitably come to rotate faster and faster, because the disc has indestructible vorticity in it as a consequence of its motion round the sun. The incoming material, drawn from further and further away as the mass of the growing planet increases, will not at first be concerned about any internal rotational difficulties that it is going to produce for the planet. But when this proceeds far enough, the primitive planets, as we may term them, will no longer be able to exist as single bodies, and their rapid rotations will tear them apart (Fig. 54). Each planet will divide into two separate main pieces, that escape completely from each other, but not necessarily from the sun, and as these recede from one another a stream of much smaller bodies will be drawn out between them, like droplets falling from something suddenly drawn out of a treacly liquid, but here the stickiness is produced by gravitational attractive forces. The nearest of them, at the two ends of the stream, will be retained by the attraction of the adjacent main bodies, and remain as satellites moving round them. But the droplets near the middle of the stream will escape from both the main separating pieces and become independent bodies.

Suppose we think of Jupiter and Saturn as the two main pieces into which a single large primitive planet originally divided. The four terrestrial planets—Mercury, Venus, the

Earth (and moon), and Mars—taken together do not amount to as much as one per cent of the mass of Jupiter. So these four comparatively tiny bodies, plus a great deal more debris too, that would go to constitute asteroids, could easily represent the "droplets" in between two separating large planets. If this explanation is correct in other respects it explains at once why the terrestrial planets are so much smaller than the great outer ones, and it could even explain why our moon is so very

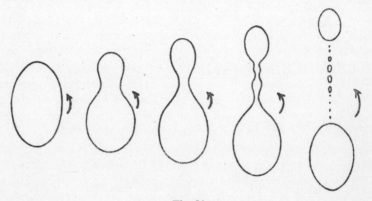

Fig. 54

Break-up of a rapidly rotating large planet: conjectural successive stages. The neck at first joining the main pieces breaks up into "droplets" to form small planets and satellites. The two main pieces separate completely from each other, but carry away some of the tiny end "droplets" as satellites. The central larger "droplets" escape from both pieces and from each other

similar in both size and mass to each of the four great moons of Jupiter. They may all have been formed adjacently in the self-same stream of material.

At first sight it might seem an objection to this description of the origin of the bodies of the solar system that the present paths of the Earth and other inner planets do not take them anywhere near Jupiter's path. But it must be remembered that it is not possible to follow out the planetary paths backwards in time for more than a few million years; beyond that stage serious divergences from the present form of paths may well begin to enter. Now the events we have been concerned with took place at least four thousand million years ago—for that as we have seen is the age of the outer layers of the Earth—and the paths of the Earth and the other inner planets could well have been sufficiently different then to pass near that of Jupiter. There are several influences operating in the solar system that would all steadily tend to make the planetary paths become more nearly circular. For instance, it must certainly not be supposed that the gradual growth of the planets would cease suddenly at the stage when the main bodies of the present planets first achieved their individuality. Although the large primitive planets would have taken the lion's share already, some of the original disc of dust particles would still remain, and also plenty of much smaller embryo planets would have formed and be doing their best to gather up what they could. But then these themselves would be in permanent danger of being collected in by the existing larger planets, and also of colliding with each other so long as their paths were not circular. The more this happened the less material would remain to be collected, and the more slowly would the process go on, either because the remaining pieces would tend to be more and more widely scattered, or if produced by collision smaller and smaller in size. But we have only to recall the surface features of the moon, where the results of large numbers of these later collisions are plain to be seen. The spring-cleaning of the solar system may well be nearing effective completion, though the existence of all the asteroids and the occasional arrival of meteorites at the Earth show that there must still be a little material left. But this whole residue now amounts to probably no more than one-thousandth of the mass of the Earth, whereas originally it must have comprised at least the whole mass of the planets, which means about five hundred Earth masses. There is therefore perhaps something like a millionth part of the original matter still circulating round the sun waiting to be picked up by the planets. Possibly in another four thousand million years' time there will be only a millionth of this left, and meteorites will then indeed be few and far between: they are rare enough now, fortunately for us.

The cumulative effect of all the collisions involved in further accretion of meteorites by a planet is a tendency to render its orbit more and more circular. The possible existence within the solar system of both dust and gaseous material, as evidenced by the zodiacal light, and all the tiny solid bodies, some of which show themselves as meteors, may also gradually operate to the same end. Almost any dissipation effects, that is processes involving loss of energy in an irreversible way, are likely to assist gradual rounding-up of the planetary orbits.

Finally there is the possible effect of the attractions of the planets on each other. Although it is at present beyond the powers of mathematical analysis to find out, it may well be that the present circular forms of the planetary paths are not permanent, but represent a condition in which such a dynamical system is most likely to be found. In other words, that highly elongated orbits would last comparatively only a short time and soon give way to less elongated ones which would persist for far longer. In that case all the various dissipation effects within the solar system would combine to steady the system into a form in which the paths never departed much from circularity. The existence of Mercury and Pluto with paths of fairly high eccentricity (about one-fifth and one-quarter, respectively) is not necessarily in conflict with this possibility, for their independent existence as planets may be comparatively recent developments, as we have seen, both of them possibly having for most of their lifetimes been satellites of their neighbouring planets, Venus and Neptune, respectively.

RADIO–ASTRONOMY

Less than twenty-five years ago the surprising discovery was made that radio-waves are reaching the Earth from outer space, and subsequent research has shown that numerous objects exist in the heavens that are acting as sources of this radiation. The power of the astronomer, hitherto restricted to study of the universe by means of ordinary light-waves, has now been given a tremendous increase, for not only can an additional survey of the outer universe be made by radio methods, but these can also penetrate to regions of our galaxy that are forever hidden to us by ordinary light through the obscuring effect of dust, which however is quite transparent where radio-waves of appropriate wave-lengths are concerned.

The energy reaches the Earth in the form of radio-waves not in any definite signal but in purely random form. It is often called "radio-noise," sounding rather like atmospherics when heard by means of an ordinary radio set.

It is now established that radio-waves are emitted by the sun itself, also by certain regions of our own galaxy and widely distributed through it, and by extra-galactic nebulae especially ones of certain abnormal type. Discrete sources, sometimes called "radio-stars," have been discovered within our own galaxy, notably in the constellations of Gemini and Cassiopeia. It is also believed that certain sources coincide with the remnants of former supernovae, the most notable example being provided by the Crab nebula itself, and there is also a weak source covering the position of the supernova of 1572.

A further weak source coincides with the position of the Andromeda nebula, the nearest of all the spiral nebulae, and a number of even weaker sources have been identified with other fairly close spiral galaxies. The radiation has also been detected from the regions of certain clusters of nebulae, notably that in Perseus which contains about five hundred individual galaxies, and that in Ursa Major which contains about three hundred. Much stronger sources however have been identified with certain abnormal external nebulae which appear to represent instances of two or more galaxies in actual collision. The separations of galaxies, unlike the stars within them, are only of order ten times their individual sizes, so that for them collisions are not remotely improbable events. The star-systems of two colliding galaxies would easily interpenetrate without colliding, the stars being so far apart, but the interstellar gas and dust of the two systems would be in collision at very high speeds, probably of order 1000 miles per second. The cause of the emission of the radio-energy is as yet very imperfectly understood, but it is believed to be a consequence of this collision of gas at high speeds. These colliding galaxies are well-distributed through the universe, and are sufficiently numerous to provide an adequate sample of the whole.

Accordingly, a survey of these objects, which with increasing instrumental power may become possible beyond the range of ordinary optical astronomical telescopes, may eventually serve to check or even extend our present knowledge of the outermost parts of the universe.

As yet at any rate, the radio-waves received do not reveal much about the nature of their sources, as ordinary light can do, for example, for a visible source by its spectrum. But on the other hand radio-waves can be made use of to investigate regions such as the centre of the galaxy that are quite inaccessible by ordinary light because of intervening dust clouds. They can also be used to survey the distribution of otherwise invisible hydrogen within our own galaxy, and to locate the arrangement of the spiral arms. In these and other ways the new techniques of radio-astronomy are therefore providing a second front of attack on many of the great problems of the astronomical universe.

REFERENCES

Astronomy, Vol. II, H. N. Russell, Ginn & Co., 1938.

Frontiers of Astronomy, F. Hoyle, Heinemann, 1955.

Radio Astronomy, A. C. B. Lovell and J. A. Clegg, Chapman and Hall, 1952.

Planispheres (showing positions of visible stars at every time of year), G. Philip & Son Ltd., London

VI

THE EXPANDING UNIVERSE

Extra-galactic nebulae or galaxies—The Andromeda nebula — Local group — Distances —
Clusters of nebulae—Number of galaxies observable—Shapes of galaxies—Why is it dark at
night?—Velocity-distance law—Expansion of the
universe—What happens beyond observable
limit?—Weakening of light owing to recession
—Olbers' paradox resolved—Are we at the
centre of the Universe?—No unique centre—
The "unobservable" galaxies—Reasons for expansion—Big-bang hypothesis—Relation to Creation—Difficulties—Continuous creation theory
—Intergalactic matter—Process of creation up for
solution — What happens to newly created
matter—Galaxies of finite age, but Universe infinitely old—Steady-state maintained—Philosophical implications.

NEBULAE OR EXTERNAL GALAXIES

We have seen that our own Milky Way system consists in the first place of stars, but so distant are even the nearest that no telescope yet constructed shows any of them to have a finite disc; each appears only as a point of light. The system also consists of tracts of interstellar gas and dust illuminated in some places by these stars. The whole goes to make up the vast swirling assembly that is our own galaxy.

But long enough ago were found many small faint patches of light occupying in the sky areas of finite size. Before any clear ideas had been formed of the distribution and location of these patches they were given the general name of *nebulae*, meaning clouds of some kind. At one time it was thought that they too were simply small patches of gas, which do in fact exist, *within* our own system, which in turn was thought to comprise the whole universe. How wrong this notion was and how restricted a concept we shall very soon see.

With the advent of great telescopes it became possible to distinguish individual stars in what eventually proved to be the nearest of these nebulae, and so the idea began to dawn that they might be other stellar systems themselves. Possibly the best known of these, and also the nearest to us, is the so-called Great Nebula in Andromeda, which alone among the nebulae is visible to a certain extent without optical aid. On a clear night the bright central part of this object can easily be seen with the unaided eye as a small hazy patch of light of about the fourth magnitude. But photography shows it to extend more than 3° across the sky—about six times the angular diameter of the moon—and it turns out that this nebula is not only the largest object in angular size in the heavens, but is also paradoxically enough the remotest astronomical object of all visible to the unaided eye.

For finding the distance of such a system the master-key is provided by the Cepheid variables. It is now possible, by means of large telescopes, to resolve the outer regions and find scores of such variables in this Andromeda nebula, and to measure their periods of light-variation accurately. In our own galaxy such stars average several thousand times as bright as the sun; but in the Andromeda nebula they appear about two hundred thousand times fainter than the faintest stars in our own sky

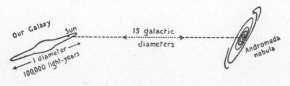

Fig. 55

The position of the Andromeda nebula in relation to our own galaxy. The nebula is to be seen in the *direction* of the constellation of Andromeda, but the stars of this constellation are in our own galaxy. The separation is about 15 diameters of either galaxy, but this part of the diagram is not to scale

that can be seen with the naked eye. The reason for this is simply their great distance, and an elementary calculation shows that this nebula must be at the immense distance of about one and a half million light-years. And this is the nearest of them all! If we think of the disc of our galaxy represented by a penny, then on the same scale the Andromeda nebula would be about a foot and a half away, but actually our galaxy itself is about a hundred thousand light-years across (Fig. 55). These values are confirmed by other types of stars that can be seen in the nebula, and the results are extremely reliable. Out to four or five million light-years similar nebulae are found in which both Cepheids and individual stars of well-known types can be identified, and these enable the distances of the extra-galactic nebulae containing them to be accurately obtained.

Accordingly these nebulae or external galaxies introduce yet another scale of distances into the universe. We began with a mere few hundred millions of miles for the planetary distances; we went on to some tens of billions of miles, or a few light-years, for the distances of the nearest stars; next we went to several thousand billion miles, or several thousand light-years, for the most distant stars in our galaxy; and now another further step for the external galaxies to millions of light-years. How far then does this continue? Are we to suppose that we have first our own stellar system, then systems of stellar systems, then higher systems still of these, and so on indefinitely? These were the sort of questions that naturally occurred to astronomers when the distances of the nebulae first began to be realised more than thirty years ago, and clearly to answer them it was necessary first actually to explore the realm of the nebulae in detail to find what happens.

This Andromeda nebula, being the nearest of all, has been one of the most closely studied, and it now turns out that it must in size be practically a twin of our own system. So if we were to imagine ourselves transported to the Andromeda nebula, and placed appropriately near a star similarly situated in it to our sun, then when we looked back to our galactic system we would see it as an object rather similar to the Andromeda nebula itself. The great band of faint light arching across the sky, which we call the Milky Way, is simply the effect of this general flattening of the system. The sun is now believed to be situated near the edge of a spiral arm, but it is proving far harder to discover and track the spiral nature of our galaxy than it is for these extra-galactic nebulae, and the positions of the arms are as yet known only very vaguely. In our own galaxy it is difficult to see the wood for the trees, since it is our very proximity that prevents us getting a view of the general structure as a whole, whereas for the extra-galactic nebulae the whole general picture can be taken in at a glance.

It has been found that there are nearly twenty galaxies more or less clustered together in our neighbourhood, of which this Andromeda nebula is one and our own another. The Magellanic clouds, though hardly ranking as galaxies themselves, are two other irregularly-shaped members of this so-called "local-group." Similarly there are lots of other clusters or groups of nebulae, and it is of great assistance in finding their distances that they happen to occur in clusters. Many of these groups contain hundreds of individual nebulae, and some even thousands. Their individual members are all sufficiently near each other to be bound together by their mutual gravitational forces, and their slightly different speeds show that they are in motion relative to each other, just as the individual stars in a star-cluster move within it under their mutual forces.

As we proceed on outwards in space, more and more nebulae are observable. If we go twice as far, we find roughly eight times as many, and so on. As far as any telescope yet constructed can reach, they are found to be approximately uniformly distributed in space, and so long as individual Cepheids can be picked out in them then the distances can be accurately found. But obviously with increasing distance it becomes harder to distinguish separate stars, and soon only the very brightest show individually.

But by the time this stage was reached in the development of the subject it had come to be recognised that the same general distribution of stars, in regard to luminosity, prevailed in all the nebulae studied to date, and was the same as in our own galaxy. So it could safely be assumed, for instance, that the brightest stars in any of these distant galaxies were intrinsically exactly as bright as the brightest in our galaxy. And this was confirmed all along the line by the Cepheid method. So even if Cepheids themselves could no longer be picked out, so long as some stars could be seen individually, these could reliably be supposed to be as bright as the very brightest stars we know of intrinsically, and their apparent brightness, or faintness really, then immediately gives a measure of their distance. Application of this procedure yields distances out to about ten million light-years. But it is found that there are still countless millions of nebulae even beyond that distance and of course appearing much fainter.

It is in finding the distances of these that the clustering property now helps, because in a cluster all the member galaxies are at effectively the same distance from us, and it can be decided at once from their relative brightnesses which of them are large nebulae, which are small ones, and which are average ones. The distances of the nearest of these cluster groups can already be found directly in the ways described, and then for much more distant groups the relative brightnesses of objects can be compared with similar nebulae in near clusters whose intrinsic brightnesses are already known, and this procedure reveals their distances. This method takes us out to distances of the order of hundreds of millions of light-years.

Finally, no matter how powerful a telescope is used, more and more nebulae come into view at greater and greater distances still. The 200-inch telescope is capable of detecting some hundred million or more galaxies. At the very limit of seeing

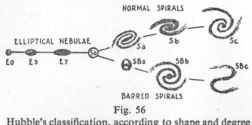

Fig. 56

Hubble's classification, according to shape and degree
of openness of arms, of the extra-galactic nebulae

(photographically by long exposures) with this instrument, faint individual galaxies are still to be found, and if it is assumed as is reasonable that they are of much the same intrinsic sizes and brightnesses as all the closer ones, then their apparent brightness, corrected to allow for a certain other effect described below, supplies us with a general measure of their distances. In this way galaxies are known to exist just as numerously at distances considerably exceeding a thousand million light-years from our own galaxy. And each of them is an object comparable with our own galaxy, consisting of individual stars each pouring out energy into space, and in this way rendering the nebula observable.

In shape these nebulae are not all of the same form, but range from being almost spherical, and therefore more or less circular in appearance, at one end of the scale to very open spiral forms at the other (Fig. 56). They have been classified, beginning with the spherical ones, first into elliptical nebulae of various degrees of elongation of figure, and then into two classes of spirals: the so-called "normal spirals," differing only by showing various degrees of openness in the windings of their arms; and the so-called "barred-spirals" which range from having the general form of a letter theta (Θ) at one end, to being rather like a letter S at the other. Some of the nebulae are of extraordinary beauty, with possibly M81 the most perfect of all, though there are claims for NGC4594, sometimes called "The Sombrero Hat." Each of them contains anything from a thousand million stars to a hundred thousand million, or even more for the very largest; and there are something like a hundred million of these objects in all within the range of modern telescopic equipment.

WHY IS IT DARK AT NIGHT?

We come now to a most extraordinary paradox. If these nebulae go on and on for ever—and with each increase of optical power they have shown not the least signs of any falling off in numbers with distance—then in whichever direction we look along a line, sooner or later we shall come to a nebula (Fig. 57). It is rather like being in a forest; no matter how widely scattered or irregularly placed, if the number of trees per square mile is roughly the same and the forest goes on for ever, then it will be impenetrable to light, so that anyone standing inside will not be able to see out. (Effects of the Earth's curvature are not relevant to the argument here.) With the nebulae, however, exactly the reverse would seem to hold, because the surface of a nebula is brilliantly luminous no matter how small it looks in the sky: so whichever way we look in the heavens we shall come to a nebula, and the sky will appear bright. The whole sky therefore ought to be brilliantly luminous; but we know for certain that it is not! This difficulty is usually referred to as Olbers' paradox, and was first noticed over a century ago. But then it was the stars that were under discussion, when it was still not known that the stars of our galaxy do not go on for ever.

What, however, is the escape from this new form of the difficulty? How does Nature avoid it? In other words, Why is it dark at night? The reason turns out to be a strange and unexpected one, and depends on another feature of the nebulae that we must now describe.

When any of them is examined by means of the spectroscope it is found that the general appearance of its light spectrum is quite similar to that of the sun, so that the various characteristic lines, particularly the dark H and K lines of calcium, are easily

Fig. 57

Illustrating Olbers' paradox. If the galaxies go on for ever in space, then whatever direction the observer O looks he will come to a galaxy at some distance or other. All regions of the sky *should* seem brilliantly luminous; but this is not so! (The diagram shows only a limited sector in one plane: actually O is surrounded on all sides in space by galaxies going on and on)

recognised, both individually, and in relation to their neighbouring lines. But in addition the nebular spectra exhibit a most startling property; the characteristic prominent dark lines of calcium are not in their expected positions, but are conspicuously displaced towards the red end of the spectrum. And the fainter the nebulae the greater is this shift of all its lines. Now according to the most reliable principles of modern physics, a shift of this kind can mean one thing and one thing only, and that is that the nebula concerned is receding from us. The fainter the nebula the greater its distance, and also the fainter the nebula the greater is this red-shift of the lines of its spectrum, and so the greater is its recessional velocity. There is evidently therefore a relation between distance and velocity, and this is now well established and known as the *velocity-distance law*. It holds for all but the very nearest of the nebulae, but these as already explained form a group with our own galaxy. Between the members of one and the same cluster the law does not hold, but only between sufficiently separated galaxies, or cluster of galaxies, these latter being regarded as single systems for the present purposes.

When this remarkable property was first vaguely come upon in the 1920's the sort of recessional speeds then indicated, for what were of course some of the nearest nebulae, were of the order of several hundred miles per second, and a few approached even a thousand miles per second. These seemed so extraordinarily large that at first many astronomers were flatly incredulous, but despite every effort to get round them the measures have since proved absolutely inescapable. Moreover with increasing powers of equipment and improved techniques, these early sensational speeds have been put entirely in the shade.

By the early 1930's further exploration at still greater distances had come on nebulae receding at speeds up to about 15,000 miles per second, nearly a tenth the velocity of light, and since then greater and greater speeds have been found. At the end of the 1930's the greatest recessional speeds determined were nearly 30,000 miles per second. During the past decade the 200-inch telescope has come into use and extended the range even further, so that velocities up to 40,000 miles per second are now fairly commonplace, and although full details are not yet available there is every likelihood of the existence of nebulae with speeds of up to about 70,000 miles per second being established soon.

Now at even the earliest stage of all these discoveries it was perceived that the velocity bore a very simple relation to the distance of the nebula concerned. If one nebula were at twice the distance of another then it was soon noticed that it had just about twice the velocity; for a nebula three times as far away as another it had three times the speed, and so on. In other words the velocity was found to be directly proportional to the distance: and this was the velocity-distance law. But since its first discovery the distances have been extended at least fifty-fold, and with every increase so far the law has continued to hold within the limits of observational uncertainty. As explained, it is now known to hold for speeds up to about a quarter of the velocity of light, and there is good reason to expect that it may soon be established up to nearly half the velocity of light. But even so it cannot definitely be inferred at this stage that it will necessarily continue on to hold for still greater speeds.

The velocity-distance law means that the whole observable universe is expanding uniformly. But it must be understood that the expansion is a large-scale motion affecting only sufficiently widely separated galaxies or clusters. The distances between the individual members of a cluster of galaxies are not affected by the expansion, which does not get under way until a distance of at least ten million light years from any particular galaxy or cluster. Local clusters, a million light-years or so across, are welded together by their own ordinary gravitation, and preserve their size absolutely; the individual galaxies and everything in them, ourselves and possessions included, remain at the same size.

The relation of velocity to distance when exhibited in the form of a diagram therefore produces a single straight line for the range of distance yet explored (Fig. 58). What this line means is easy to understand, for if we are given the distance of any particular nebula, this has only to be read off against the line and the corresponding velocity is obtained, and vice versa. In Fig. 58 the continuous part of the line represents the part definitely settled, and checked over and over again by various means. This extends to speeds of nearly a quarter the speed of light. The next part, drawn in heavy dashes, represents the part that is still being investigated and which so far shows some signs of conforming to the straight-line law. With modern equipment the maximum distance to which it should eventually be possible to study the law would correspond to a speed of almost half that of light.

The question of what happens beyond the limitations set by present day equipment can clearly only be settled theoretically until such time as the direct verification at greater ranges still can be made. The simplest possibility, and the one most strongly suggested by successive extensions of the range, is

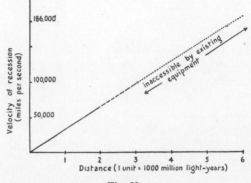

Fig. 58

The velocity-distance law. The solid line corresponds to the already verified portion of the law and the adjacent broken line to the part that is yet to be verified but probably accessible with existing equipment. This may eventually extend to a distance corresponding to about half the speed of light. The dotted line corresponds to the region unlikely to be accessible with any existing equipment

that the velocity-distance law simply carries on linearly; in other words that the graph of velocity against distance continues on as a straight line. But if this happens, there will be a finite distance at which the corresponding speed of recession is that of light itself, and for reasons to be explained below, this would place an absolute limit on the size of the observable universe beyond which no equipment, however powerful or ingenious, could ever penetrate. This distance, according to the most up-to-date observational evidence, is about six thousand million light years, but there is no immediate prospect of observation of anything beyond about half this critical distance, and successive further observational steps into outer space will require very much greater increases in telescope size than the mere increase in distance would suggest for reasons next to be explained.

WEAKENING OF LIGHT OWING TO THE RECESSION

It has been seen how these great speeds show themselves through the displacement of the spectral lines of the light of the nebula towards the red. But in addition to this, the recessional speed weakens the whole intensity of the light of the nebula, and makes its total light as received here *less* than what it would be if the nebula were at rest at the same distance. The factor of reduction is calculable by pure theory for any given speed of recession, just as can the red-shift of the spectral lines, and so is known independently of the observations to which it is to be applied (Fig. 59). At a velocity corresponding to a distance of about one thousand million light-years, the factor of reduction is about two-thirds; that is, the nebula is seen here only two-thirds as bright in total light as if it were at rest at the same distance. For a nebula at about three thousand million light-years, its light is reduced to about one-third by this effect; the speeds of such nebulae would be just about half the velocity of light. For velocities even greater than this the reduction is still larger, until finally if a nebula were receding from us with the velocity of light its total intensity would be reduced to zero; and therefore we could never see it! If the velocity-distance relation should continue on linearly to the speed of light, this velocity would be reached at a distance of about six thousand million light-years.

On this basis, or on any other for which the velocity continues to increase with distance, every receding object has its total light (that we receive) reduced more and more with the increase of speed, and therefore nebulae become decreasingly visible, until finally as the velocity of light is approached they are no longer visible at all! This is the way Olbers' paradox is so unexpectedly resolved. There may conceptually be a nebula in whatever direction we look, but after a certain distance no light could reach us from it because of its speed. And we reach the surprising conclusion that our sky is dark at night because the universe is expanding! Thus is it seen how events at the remotest parts of the universe can affect conditions for us here on Earth.

According to this theoretical picture of the universe there would appear to exist an infinity of galaxies lying beyond this

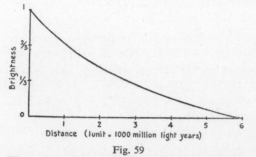

Fig. 59

Weakening of light owing to recessional speeds. The curve shows the factor by which the brightness, as observed, is decreased as compared with the brightness if the nebula were at rest at the same distance. At the speed of light the reduction would be to zero

critical distance corresponding to the velocity of light. But though the conceptual model allows them to enter, they must be regarded as such that by no conceivable physical means could we ever receive any signals from these objects. The distances between us and them are increasing faster than the speed of light, and for this reason we can never perform any experiment to become aware of anything going on in su h galaxies. This means that they are *outside* of our universe, and so cannot be regarded as having any physical existence for us. The crucial distance beyond which they all lie is a kind of horizon, but in all directions, of our accessible universe, and we, the observer, are at the centre. The objects within this distance are receding from us faster and faster as we proceed outwards in our mind's eye, and get fainter and fainter at an even faster rate than the pure distance effect would give because of their recessional speeds. As the limit is approached they approach complete invisibility, and beyond that is not within the domain of the physical universe.

ARE WE AT THE CENTRE OF THE UNIVERSE?

Now, all this begins to look as if we are at a unique centre of the universe after all, with man restored once again to the unique position he was formerly so anxious always to give himself. But this is not really so. Supposing we imagine ourselves transported to another galaxy inside the theoretical observable limit of our universe, which if the velocity-distance law continues to hold we can suppose lies six thousand million light-years away. Then for an observer there, our galaxy would seem to be receding from him in the opposite direction in space at just the same speed, and around him all the visible galaxies would exhibit exactly the same velocity-distance law out to a distance from him of precisely the same amount. And he could equally well maintain that he was at the centre of the universe. And both would be right. Every observer, in whatever galaxy he happened to be situated, would get the same overall picture of the universe and would arrive at the same velocity-distance law. Only the details of the distribution of the nebulae in their respective skies would be different to them in their different galaxies. The large-scale appearance and behaviour of the universe would be the same for them all.

We could make a simple but incomplete analogy by thinking of observers at different points on the surface of the Earth and able to increase their range of view by mounting up a high tower. Each could see the surface out to a certain distance, and this horizon will be a circle to the observer, who will be at its centre. And every other observer at a different place will have his circular horizon. But the details of the Earth's surface that each sees will not be the same except for parts that may overlap, and these parts they will see from different viewpoints and so see different aspects of them. There is of course no expansion in this analogy, but we could even introduce that feature if we

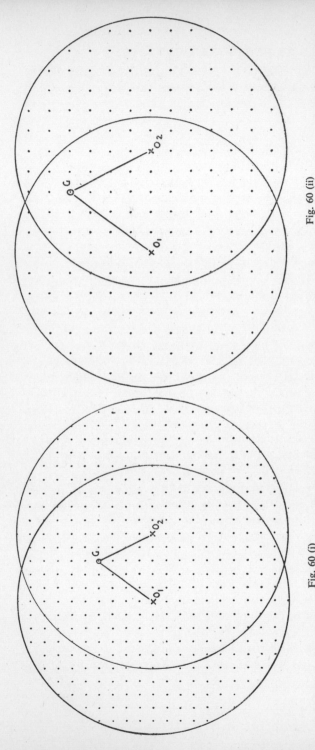

Fig. 60 (i)

A two-dimensional model of the universe. Two observers O_1 and O_2 are at their own different "centres" of their observable universes. The dots represent galaxies (in reality they are only equally-spaced on average). The circles represent the "horizons" of observation for observers in the two galaxies. The dots are supposed to go on for ever; so O_1 or O_2 (or any other point) can be regarded as the centre and will appear to be so from observations made there

Fig. 60 (ii)

A two-dimensional "expanding universe." This shows the same system with every distance between galaxies increased $1\frac{1}{2}$ times. If O_1 is superposed on the point O_1 of the previous figure, every other point, such as G, will have moved directly away from O_1 by 50%. But equally so, if O_2 is placed on the previous position of O_2 exactly the same still holds and the expansion is directly away from O_2. This diagram shows a thinning out of points (galaxies) owing to the expansion (as must happen on the "explosion" hypothesis), but new galaxies are forming to maintain the actual number unchanged on average in the "steady-state" theory imagined the Earth to be a vast balloon that was being blown up. But in the actual case of the galaxies that we are concerned with the world is three-dimensional and the observer's horizon is a sphere.

The one thing that has to be emphasised about this general expansion is that it has no unique centre; any point of the universe can equally well be regarded as the centre of expansion. We could make a working model of the universe consisting of a lattice of beads spaced out in three-dimensions and joined by uniform elastic strings. The only defect is that such a model must have a limited size and possess boundaries somewhere, whereas in the actual universe there is no corresponding boundary, though there is a limit, as we have explained, to the distance that we can see no matter how powerful a means we used. When all the strings of the model are stretched in the same proportion that would represent an expansion of the universe (Fig. 60). And if we fix attention on a particular bead and then expand the model, all the other beads will appear to move directly away from it, irrespective of whether the beads are regularly spaced out or not. Also, the displacement of any particular bead away from the original bead will be proportional to its distance. But now if we start at another bead altogether, exactly the same expansion will seem to be directly away from it, and again the amount of expansion is proportional to the distance from this bead. So you see whichever bead we happened to live in, we would regard the expansion as directly away from us, but we would have no reason to dissent if someone living in another bead insisted on regarding the expansion as directly away from him. Both would be right. We can sum up the two observers' positions by saying that the whole universe is expanding uniformly at all its parts, and that all points may be regarded equally as a centre of the expansion.

THE "UNOBSERVABLE" GALAXIES

Now perhaps a little more should be said about the galaxies that according to these ideas would seem to lie beyond the horizon and therefore could never be detected. Do they really exist? Scientifically their existence cannot be established by any physical means, practical or conceivable, and so cannot ever be directly settled. But in the mind of astronomers, particularly the theoretical astronomers, they do have an existence as part of the conceptual model needed to describe those parts of the universe that *are* accessible. If one accepts that description of the universe then the conceptual existence of these undetectable galaxies goes with it, but they can never have any influence on the part of the universe where the observer lives because no physical processes of any kind can ever travel from them to the observer or vice versa. So the entire physical universe that need or can be taken into account by us is that lying within this horizon-sphere surrounding us. One hopes the reader will find that satisfactory and not feel that science is restricting things too much by excluding the region beyond. There are probably many thousands of millions of galaxies within this sphere, each of them containing something like the number of stars that our own galaxy contains, and perhaps even containing a few stars with attendant planets moving round them. So it is pretty rich in content and there will be scope for Nature to play out unimaginable dramas elsewhere than on Earth in this universe. Think how much goes on on the surface of this tiny planet of ours; who would believe it if one did not know it really happens.

Now all these speeds, and distances, and large numbers, that enter into the description of the realm of the nebulae, certainly seem incredible when one first hears of them, but it is to be remembered that they are nowadays mere commonplace facts in the world of astronomy. Their proof depends on scientific principles as well established as those on which the working of modern scientific equipment and machinery depends, and if it were possible to take you, dear reader, by the hand as it were and lead you step by step from the things that you are familiar with in everyday life through the various stages that are involved in establishing these things, you would find complete certainty at every point, and end by feeling not one shadow of doubt that the picture that has been described is indeed inevitable. We know this, because many highly critical minds have gone over all the various steps time and time again, and tested them out, and verified them by other means and yet others, and have emerged from it all completely convinced. And so I think would you. Therefore you may rely on it that this is no fancy fairy story but the stark reality, in so far as we admit reality.

REASONS FOR THE EXPANSION

However, these are only what we may term the facts, but where the really interesting and even more exciting part of the work begins is when we come to try to interpret the meaning of the expansion. What human intellect desires is some theory that accounts for it, or explains it, just as the theory of gravitation accounts for the motion of the planets round the sun, and enables predictions of their future positions to be made. Now there have been several interesting preliminary attempts to deal theoretically with the present problem of varying degrees of simplicity; but for reasons of space the discussion will be confined to just two of the proposed theories.

The first of them has been termed the 'big-bang' hypothesis. Suppose in our mind's eye we imagine time running backwards instead of forwards, then all the nebulae instead of moving away from each other will obviously start to crowd together. If this is allowed to go on for about six thousand million years, all the nebulae within the (technically) observable universe will have come close together. That is, all the matter of the universe it would seem must have originated in a very small region of space compared with the volume the nebulae are now spread through. This has suggested the idea that perhaps the universe originated in a gigantic explosion, six or seven thousand million years ago, in which the material that now forms the galaxies was thrown apart with speeds of all values up to the velocity of light itself. The explosion would have to be regarded as a kind of singular initial event in the history of the universe; what it was like before the explosion took place it would not be possible to say. But postulate the "big-bang," and with it the instantaneous creation of all the matter of the universe, and then something like the present distribution might follow. The velocity-distance relation seems very readily to be explained by this theory. For if we consider two pieces resulting from the explosion, one of which is thrown out with twice the speed of the other, then clearly after a lapse of a given time interval it will have got twice as far, and so their distances will be proportional to their respective velocities. The same will hold for any other speed, just as in a horse-race it is the fastest that are out in front. Thus the explosion idea has no serious difficulty up to a point in accounting at least approximately for this observed feature of the universe.

A theory such as this that puts back creation to a singular instant in the remote past is in its nature difficult to prove or disprove (though not necessarily impossible), but to some minds it is an objection that it would imply the removal of the question of the origin of the material of the universe from the realm of science. If the theory were correct, it would mean that we would just have to swallow this and learn to accept that we would never be able to initiate any successful enquiry into how the initial catastrophe (no moral judgment being implied by the word) came to happen. On the other hand many minds, perhaps the majority at present, feel quite the reverse, and seem only too relieved that something may be spared from the fearsome encroachments of science into every domain. This consideration does not of course mean that the explosion theory is necessarily wrong, but it puts the act of Creation, as we might term it, beyond the reach of science. Now in questions of this sort when they are in their early stages of development, and this one is very much so, scientists are forced to use what processes of judgment they can to guide them as between one idea and another. The problem develops a kind of aesthetic basis, and some deeper instinct has to be used to guide us aright and save us from wasting too much time in investigating, or being satisfied with, ideas that in fact are blind alleys. Modern science is so vast and intricate that it is only by cultivation of this instinct, or by original possession of it, that it is possible to steer a way through and arrive at important results. But it is precisely as a result of this feature that new advances in science, particularly on the purely theoretical side, are so fraught with controversy, because different people's aesthetic senses, which have their roots deep down in emotion and temperament, are apt to guide them in very different ways, and what to one seems a most enlightened mode of approach to a problem will fill another, it seems, with feelings of the utmost repugnance. The present problem has not been free of this element, and bitter controversy has surrounded it with waxing and waning degrees of severity over this past thirty years or so.

However, serious difficulties of several kinds are already looming into view in regard to the explosion hypothesis, some of which if fully established may afford a decisive test. For instance, according to the theory, the general distribution of all the elements, in particular the heaviest, was set up once and for all (apart from the conversion of hydrogen to helium that keeps the stars shining) during the initial stages of the explosion occupying the first twenty minutes of the existence of the universe; so that the cookery of the elements was achieved in "less time than it takes to do roast-duck and potatoes" in Gamow's homely phrase. Thus on this view, all stars would now be expected to show the same concentration of these heaviest elements, and the fact that this is not the case seems to tell heavily against the hypothesis, until some additional explanation overcoming this is presented. Again, the theory has yet to cope with the extremely difficult question of why condensation of the material into galaxies and stars should have set in only after the density of matter in space had fallen to the infinitesimally low value (of order at most 10^{-24} gm. per cm^3.) at which observation suggests it does occur, when it would seem that at the far higher densities prevailing earlier on, according to the theory, the possibility of condensation would be correspondingly greater.

Then again, in a different category perhaps, another objection arises if we consider for instance what will come to pass in the future as the expansion continues. Sooner or later, with the exception of the few local systems that form a cluster with our own galaxy, all the rest of the nebulae will have disappeared from sight (even with the most powerful telescope) and space will be practically empty; the several hundred million galaxies that we can still observe will all have gone. This would mean that we see them now simply because we happen to live at this time in a comparatively early stage of the expansion. Wait a few more thousand million years, and if there are any astronomers in our galaxy, then no matter what equipment they can invent they will find nothing beyond the few local galaxies of our immediate group of neighbours. One wonders what they would make of it. Does that idea appeal to you? Possibly it has been put in words that are apt to prejudice because it does not appeal to the writer, who at the time of writing does not quite like this picture of what is going to happen, even though it probably will not concern him much what the universe may look like several thousand million years hence.

But in view of the expansion what else is possible? This is a question that has received considerable attention, and now quite recently there has been suggested an entirely different picture of the development of the universe that for some astronomers has special attractions, and seems to hold out much more hope of being on the right lines.

If we do in fact feel that the emptying of space is an unsatisfactory prospect, yet we cannot bring ourselves to deny or evade the direct evidence of the radial expansion, may it not be possible to introduce the idea of *continual creation* of matter in the world, going on at the present time and all the time, to just such an extent that makes up for the loss of matter through galaxies that disappear over the horizon? May it not be that it is a property of space that wherever space occurs then matter may appear in it *from nowhere*, and to just such an extent in total throughout the observable universe as to balance the loss over the frontier horizon of the universe? That is new material, created from nothing, throughout space.

We have been brought up to think of the permanence and indestructibility of matter—the conservation of matter—but the rate of creation required by this hypothesis would be far less than anything that could be detected by any experiment yet practicable in any terrestrial laboratory. The requisite rate is not difficult to work out because it is known roughly how much matter there is in a typical one of the galaxies and also the rate of their disappearance. Spread through the whole of space the requisite rate of creation turns out to be minutely small. Take for instance a large building like St Paul's cathedral; then if one hydrogen atom originated every thousand years within it, that would be about the rate throughout the universe needed to offset the loss by the departing galaxies. Every similar volume of space would of course on average have to be keeping up the same rate of creation of matter. In the room in which you may be sitting the rate would perhaps be one hydrogen atom every hundred thousand years. So no one would be likely to notice it, even if an atom were created right now. The principle of conservation of matter, so sacrosanct in science, it must always be remembered is, like any other principle, established only within certain experimental limits, and they are far cruder than the departure from strict conservation that this minute rate of creation implies. So there is no suggestion of any serious upset of any of the already established things in science by the introduction of the idea of continuous creation. It is a permissible development from the existing framework of science that a new realm of observation—the receding galaxies—suggests may be necessary. And this sort of new step is exactly in accordance with the procedure of the development of science.

Now this theory can in fact be set up in mathematical form, as all good theories can, and it turns out in the theory that the rate of expansion of the universe is directly connected with the rate of origin of matter, and vice versa. It is the origination of matter in space that causes the expansion; this is what the theory shows. Now it seems most unlikely that the new matter appears only at set places in space where there is already matter, because new galaxies to replace the disappearing ones would not thereby happen but only an addition of matter to already existing galaxies. Rather it seems from the theory that its appearance is a property of space itself, and that the matter appears at points spread uniformly through the whole of space.

This would mean that intergalactic space must also itself be occupied by matter in the form of primitive hydrogen, and the theory suggests its density to be about 10^{-27} of that of water; that is one gram would be contained in a cube of side 10^9 centimetres, or ten thousand kilometres. (This is about equal to the volume of the whole Earth.) A comparable volume of space *within* a galaxy contains about one ton (or a million grams) on average.

Thus whatever way we approach this phenomenon of the expansion of the universe it inevitably leads us to the fundamental question of creation itself. What has happened is that physical science, after a mere three hundred years or so of considerably restricted endeavour and existence, has nevertheless achieved the great triumph of coming face to face with this hitherto most inscrutable of questions, namely that of the process of creation of matter. It is now plainly on the agenda of science for discussion and eventual solution, if man survives. But please do not suppose that the problem is solved: very far from it. It is only just broached and scientists are still struggling to get the right attitude to it.

But as we have seen the picture that is now insistently presenting itself is, that as a result of the galaxies moving apart, an amount of matter (hydrogen again it must be) is created from nothing in the space between them at just such a rate as to compensate for the general decrease that would otherwise be produced by the expansion. To take a very simple analogy, think of a bucket of water and suppose it steadily supplied by rain from above (Fig. 61). Then, however it is started off, and no matter what small disturbances occur, the water will eventually come to stream out over the sides at precisely the same rate that the rain is supplying it. The water spilling over represents the disappearing galaxies, and the rain from above represents the newly created matter. But in the actual case, the new material just does not exist physically before it appears in space from nowhere.

Now what happens to this newly created matter? According to the theory it aggregates itself together by ordinary gravitational attraction and forms new galaxies, which in turn produce within themselves stars requiring hydrogen for the purpose of their energy generation, so that instead of space gradually being cleared of galaxies, as the explosion hypothesis would need, fresh ones are forever being formed to maintain the same average distribution. So if we ourselves could be born again in many thousand million years' time, there would still be just as many galaxies in the sky to be seen, but the details of their arrangement in the heavens would be different from

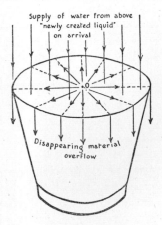

Fig. 61

A two-dimensional model of the "con-
tinual-creation" theory.

The observable universe to a "flat-man" living at O is the upper surface of the water in the bucket. The rain falling from above would simply "appear" to him from "nowhere" in his world. An equal amount would vanish over the rim, which would be his "horizon" in his (flat) space. Also the outwards velocity of the liquid at *any* point of the upper surface (his universe) will be proportional to the distance from O and it will also depend on the rate of "creation of new matter," changing in proportion to it

that of the present ones. We can liken the situation to a forest in which new small trees are constantly coming on, and a selection of all the others always being removed. The forest can go on existing forever and will always look very much the same; yet none of its members need be as old as the forest itself; in one sense the forest is always changing, but in another it is always the same.

Similarly in this theory of the universe: only the elements that go to make up the universe have finite ages, that is the galaxies themselves; the universe itself has no beginning and no end. It has always existed, and is therefore infinitely old. The question of how the universe started does not arise. However far we look back in time the same general situation would hold, and to an observer in a galaxy like ours, say, the general appearance of the surrounding universe would always be much the same; only the details would change. Also, it would not matter where in the universe the observer happened to be; he would be able to regard himself as at the centre of it, and find all the other galaxies streaming away from him in the manner already described with velocity everywhere proportional to the distance. For these reasons this description has been termed the *steady-state* theory of the universe; although change is going on everywhere, the general overall situation always remains very much the same. As it was in the beginning, is now, and ever shall be: world without end.—Except that there was no beginning. It is rather like watching a small stretch of river: every part is moving and will disappear from us, only to be replaced and invisibly resupplied, so that the river itself seems always much the same, and indeed this is how we always think of a river. But where the universe is concerned, we are on or in one of the galaxies and that part is not carried away from us ever. On this theory the velocities are proportional to the distances and increase with them, so that allowance for the time that light takes to get here makes no difference to the velocity-distance law. For the explosion hypothesis, with the speeds remaining constant, a correction of the observations is necessarily of increasing importance as the speeds approach that of light.

Now another thing that this theory promises is to some minds one of its greatest sources of appeal. It brings the question of the process of creation of matter right into the centre of the scientific arena, a process hitherto altogether excluded. We know there is matter in the universe, and it must have originated somehow. But if its appearance is consigned to some unanalysable fundamental explosion of the kind described above, it would seem to follow that we shall be precluded forever of knowing anything about how it happened. But now how much more hopeful is this second theory! It means that creation may be going on around us all the time; that it may be some fundamental property of space itself; and if this is so then the ingenuity of man may sooner or later come to understand it, and find its relation to the ultimate structure of matter. But we cannot say what more may come with it because at present we have only arrived at the very beginnings of the idea. These as we have said are the sort of aesthetic considerations that urge men of science to prefer one idea to another in its early stages, and the general hypothesis of continual creation is being actively thought about by a number of scientists today, and will probably be thought about by a great many more as its popularity gains. But it will take time. Here may be a clue to one of Nature's most fundamental processes of all, and we must not expect that it is likely to give up its deep secrets easily.

.   .   .   .   .   .

Although this completes our account of the astronomical topics we set out to review, it does not seem possible to end simply on this note after describing the astounding picture of the universe as a whole that modern scientific and astronomical research has revealed. In all these questions it is not possible, save in highly technical works, to go into things in the detail they really require for their full explanation. To give only one instance, an apparently simple thing like the distance of the sun requires something like ten years for a worthwhile modern refined value to be derived, and moreover the necessary observations can be undertaken only at favourable positions of the tiny planet Eros, which occur infrequently only every thirty years or more. Many problems are of even more extensive a character. But there is no doubt, as we have said, that anyone prepared to take the necessary trouble could proceed step by step from the ideas that he is familiar with to those involved in modern science, and it would be possible for him to see beyond any shadow of doubt that this mysterious universe that surrounds us is in fact as vast and rich in content, and as prodigal of matter and energy, as these pages have attempted to explain.

There is one final question that occurs to us all in response to some deep cosmic emotion when we are confronted at whatever level by the wonder of the universe, and one that has so often been asked before, namely, "What is the meaning and object of it all?" This is the question that down the ages has puzzled all the thinkers and all the philosophers without any real satisfactory answer being found. And now it seems only Science is left to appeal to, and what science says is that there is no indication whatsoever in the whole cosmos that there is any discernible purpose at all.

Even though some deep inner voice says otherwise and prompts us that there must be, we have to be on our guard. These are the very kind of feelings that go so far to undo us when it comes to the steps needed for new advances in thought. But in any case, as we well know, mankind has already been led to so much disaster that he did not wish for by listening to this same inner voice. Ideas or beliefs cannot with value be accepted simply in their own right by a process of vehement adherence to them, and our only hope in any of these matters lies in preserving an impassive calm that enables us to adopt a rational approach at all times, believing in nothing and yet rejecting nothing until we have adequate evidence to guide us, and even then always retaining some element of doubt in our minds that enables us to be ready for the next stage of advancement of thought, however firmly established former ideas may seem.

And it is from this rational approach that has been distilled this seemingly fantastic conception of the universe, in which are occurring these cosmic events on a scale almost beyond belief, were they not so inescapably established, involving the raw materials of the firmament in their most fundamental forms. Here the secrets of nature are being disclosed—as Jeans truly said many years ago "The story of the atom is written across the sky"—and surely it is the least we can do to take advantage of these gifts of nature in the hope of coming to understand more fully the world in which we live.

REFERENCES

The Realm of the Nebulae, E. Hubble, Oxford, 1936.
Cosmology, H. Bondi, Cambridge, 1952.
The Expanding Universe, A. S. Eddington, Cambridge, 1933.